STATISTICAL GEOGRAPHY: Problems in Analyzing Areal Data

# Statistical

# Geography

*Problems in Analyzing Areal Data*

*By Otis Dudley Duncan, Ray P. Cuzzort, and Beverly Duncan*

THE FREE PRESS OF GLENCOE, ILLINOIS

# PREFACE

A BY-PRODUCT of several years of research on areal problems, this monograph was written at the suggestion of Dr. Harvey S. Perloff, Director of the Program of Regional Studies, Resources for the Future, Inc. During 1956-57 we had the pleasure of collaborating with Dr. Perloff's unit in connection with a study of "Natural Resources and Regional Economic Growth," the results of which are now available in other publications. Upon the completion of our contribution (having to do with areal variation in levels of living and spatial patterns of economic activity) to that project we seemed to have accumulated a collection of methodological conundrums which were perhaps worth sharing with other research workers; but these could not be expounded conveniently along with substantive findings. Although this circumstance occasioned the writing of the present volume, in preparing a separate statement on method we have broadened the scope considerably beyond the issues arising in any single project, drawing upon our own earlier experience and a rich but scattered literature.

For a group of sociologists to write on *Statistical Geography* may seem somewhat incongruous. If so, we hope the consequence is what Kenneth Burke called "perspective by incongruity." It will quickly become apparent to the reader that "statistical geography" refers to a set of methodological problems and not to any unique body of subject matter which representatives of a particular discipline are best equipped to investigate. Actually, on occasion we have heard geographers refer to our own studies as having some geographic interest; assuming such remarks are intended to be complimentary, we have interpreted them that way. Though our mastery of the methodological literature in geography is manifestly incomplete—only after the first draft of this study was written, for example, did we become familiar with the interesting series of Lund Studies in Human Geography— we can only hope that geographers may learn from our efforts as we have learned from their contributions. More generally we hope that each of the social sciences will begin to realize more fully the advantages to be gained from studying the others' methodological developments in respect to the analysis of areal data.

We must acknowledge with thanks the valuable suggestions and criticisms vouchsafed us by Brian J. L. Berry, James M. Beshers, George H. Borts, Otis Durant Duncan, William L. Garrison, Leo A. Goodman, Zvi Griliches, Philip M. Hauser, Amos H. Hawley, H. H. McCarty, Richard F. Muth, Albert J. Reiss, Jr., and Arthur H. Robinson. None of these persons, how-

ever, has read the manuscript in final draft and none, of course,
is responsible for the uses to which we have put his comments.
We owe a special acknowledgement to Donald J. Bogue, whose
work in statistical geography so often has been an inspiration
as well as a point of departure for our own. Needless to say,
neither he nor any other colleague will endorse every statement
we make. For financial support of the preparation and publication of this volume (as well as the antecedent study mentioned
above), we are grateful to Resources for the Future, Inc. Harvey
Perloff's encouragement and enthusiasm were no less essential to
its completion. We are also indebted to the Social Science Research Committee of the University of Chicago for financial support, particularly in connection with computations reported in
sections 3.1 and 3.5.

OTIS DUDLEY DUNCAN
RAY P. CUZZORT
BEVERLY DUNCAN

# CONTENTS

# FIGURES

# TABLES

STATISTICAL GEOGRAPHY: Problems in Analyzing Areal Data

# CHAPTER 1

# PRELIMINARIES

Of method much is written.
With method little is done.
—*Arthur F. Bentley*

DOES discussion of methodology for its own sake enable science to progress more rapidly than it could by eschewing such discussion? The question is a little like the one of whether a man can raise himself by his bootstraps or—in the biblical phrase—"by taking thought can add one cubit unto his stature." There is such a surfeit of methodological literature in the social sciences that one who proposes to contribute an increment thereto is well advised to make his apologies in advance. Our apologies run along conventional lines. We doubt that purely formal or philosophical analyses of methodological questions do much to ease the day-to-day labors of the scientist in the field or laboratory, although their long run significance may be as great as it is intangible. It is apparent, however, that the history of science reveals numerous instances of the transfer of methods between disciplines not closely related by subject matter. Most of us can report cases in which we learned a better way of attacking our own research problems by studying how the other fellow grappled with his. It is a striking fact, too, that certain methodological problems are solved independently by investigators working without knowledge of the parallel contributions of others. Possibly this kind of waste motion could be reduced if the process of communicating methodological developments across disciplinary boundaries were made more explicit and systematic.

To get down to cases, we note that research workers in a number of fields are encountering analogous problems in making inferences from statistical data ordered by areal units. In some instances there is a convergence of different disciplines on a particular substantive problem and a consequent similarity of methodological problems in the several disciplines. In other cases, one can readily observe the kind of methodological parallelism just mentioned when technically similar, though substantively different, problems are encountered in such diverse subjects as economic geography, plant ecology, agricultural economics, and urban sociology. The extraordinary recent growth of an organization called the "Regional Science Association" seems to be attributable to the recognition of a community of methodological interests embracing scholars from a variety of fields rather than to any agreement on a frame of reference for studies of the "region" in a substantive sense (cf. James, 1958). In any case, the fact that a good many social scientists have suddenly discovered they are "regional scientists" reflects an increasing preoccupation with spatial and areal problems on the part of disciplines hitherto little inclined to regard such problems as fundamental. It may also adumbrate the emergence of a more explicit, more formal, and better codified collection of tools for accomplishing the kinds of analytical tasks which these disciplines have in common. The present monograph is perhaps best described as a pilot investigation of the feasibility of such formalization and codification.

It is instructive to observe the similarity of the present situation regarding the treatment of areal data to that existing some decades ago in respect to temporally ordered data. Statisticians have made use of time series almost as long as statistical data have been collected. But as these data became more voluminous and as the theory of statistical inference developed, it was noted, for example, that statistical procedures invented to deal with biometric data—where comparisons have to do with individual organisms making up a population—might lead to equivocal results when applied to comparisons among years. Thus papers came to be written under such titles as "Why Do We Sometimes Get Nonsense Correlations Between Time Series?" Meanwhile, workers in various fields, e.g., agricultural scientists working on weather-crop hypotheses, economists seeking explanations of business cycles, and biologists examining growth sequences, were devising new means of treating time series data. The techniques of time series analysis were recognized as having such broad application that nearly every statistics text included a special treatment of them. Specialized texts and monographs on the subject were written. Special compilations of economic and social data under such titles as "Historical Statistics" appeared. In fields where many of the available data took the form of time series it became customary to warn of the pitfalls in their analysis when embarking on a study. Although few statisticians and research workers would contend that currently available techniques of time series analysis are satisfactory in all respects, the investigator undertaking a time series study is not without resources if he wishes to capitalize on the experience of others.

In geography—the discipline where areal data are the stock in trade—a comparable evolution has doubtless occurred, insofar as cartographic techniques are concerned. But the situation of the topic surveyed by the present monograph—which we may perhaps call "statistical geography" for short—is rather different. Until rather recent times geographers have not given a great deal of attention to statistical methods. Systematic interest in spatial or areal problems seems to have emerged rather slowly in the social sciences until a similarly recent period. Workers in each discipline seem not to be well acquainted with pertinent methodological developments in the others. There are no textbooks on "space series" techniques analogous to those on time series, and only a few general texts on statistics call the special features of areal data to the student's attention. Much of the statistical research on geographic distributions, areal variation, and spatial relationships gives evidence of methodological improvisation and *ad hoc* adaptation of techniques originally devised for other sorts of problems.

It would appear that a pilot investigation of the feasibility of formalizing and codifying methods of analyzing areal data should concern itself with the following problems. It should first identify the major kinds of interest in the analysis of areal data which have emerged in various disciplines and the characteristic methodological problems introduced by those interests. Then it should consider carefully what the basic features of areal data are that have special relevance for the way these data are to be analyzed, giving attention to the kinds of operations by which areal data are generated. Finally, it should essay an inventory of some of the more significant analytical problems, as they have been encountered by research workers to date, and indicate the lines along which solutions to these problems are being sought. That a "pilot investigation" should accomplish all these tasks adequately is not to be expected, and we can only hope that the reader's expectations are as modest as ours. But a beginning needs to be made somewhere, and a collection of working notes aimed toward the eventual codification of methods in statistical geography may be expected to contain at least a few items with suggestive value for those who share this aim. Our task is made lighter than it would be otherwise by the fact that some initial steps toward codifying methods of statistical geography already have been taken (e.g., Goodall, 1952; Bogue and Harris, 1954; Shevky and Bell, 1955; Hauser, Duncan, and Duncan, 1956; Reynolds, 1956; Bachi, 1958; Greig-Smith, 1957; Stewart and Warntz, 1958). These partial summaries and critical reviews of portions of our subject provide evidence that our interest is not an idiosyncratic one.

## 1.1. Parallel and Converging Developments

No doubt the foregoing brief assessment of the current situation in statistical geography will seem somewhat abstract and overgeneralized. Hence we wish to set down quickly some salient illustrations of the methodological parallels and convergences to which reference was made. Certain of the problems mentioned here will be treated in more detail in later sections, and in section 1.2 we shall set forth a more formal and comprehensive classification of approaches to the analysis of areal data. Here we wish simply to call attention to the resemblances among problems being faced in the several fields having like or common interests in statistical geography.

Under the heading of "parallel developments" we give illustrations of ways in which similar methodological problems have been handled in studies dealing with diverse subject matter. Oftentimes these parallels occur when investigators independently work out formally identical techniques. In other instances there is transfer of analytical methods between fields, but it is rare that workers in a given field gain as much from such transfers as they could by more extensive study of the methodological parallels.

The first illustration of a methodological parallel concerns the development of measures of areal distribution and areal association in studies in location economics, population geography, plant ecology, and urban sociology. The problem has to do with measuring the degree of areal concentration of a sub-population with respect to the total population of which it is a part, or the degree of areal association between two populations or sub-populations. The term "population" is here understood to refer to any collection of such units as business establishments, churches, or schools as well as a collection of individual plants, animals, or human beings. Hoover (1936) and Florence (*et al.*, 1943) introduced to location economists such measures as "location quotients," "coefficients of localization," and "coefficients of geographic association." Their work in this field has been followed up by Thompson (1953) among others. Meanwhile, Wright (1937) presented to geographers a system for measuring distributions which involved some of the same indexes and some closely related thereto. More recently, urban sociologists developed a considerable literature on "segregation indexes," several of which are formally identical with one or another of the measures suggested by Hoover, Florence, and Wright. (A key paper in this series was published by Jahn *et al.*, 1947; further developments are considered by Duncan and Duncan, 1955a,b, and Bell and Willis, 1957.) Significantly enough, every now and then investigators start all over again to invent segregation indexes, seemingly without referring to the available literature (e.g., Hutchinson, 1956, Chapter 3). As far as we know, the use of some of the same measures of concentration and association in plant ecology (Goodall, 1952; Kontkanen, 1957) was developed without reference to any of the literature in geography, economics, and sociology.

A broader kind of problem where parallelism can be seen has to do with statistical inference. In one form of this problem, the issue is as follows: Can inferences about relationships drawn from areal data be applied to units other than areas? For example, if a statistician computes the proportion of the population which is of foreign birth in each census tract of a city and correlates it with the census tract proportion of home owners, finding a positive relationship, can he conclude that the foreign born are more likely than the natives to own their homes? Much early work on voting statistics appeared to assume that such inferences are justified, although no mathematical rationale for them was available. It was pointed out by W. S. Robinson in 1950 that they are not mathematically justified, and that individual relationships inferred from areal correlations may be seriously biased as to magnitude and even erroneous as to sign. The clearest parallel is with work in economics concerning the "aggregation problem," one aspect of which is the question of whether relationships based on "macro-economic" data will be consistent with relationships ascertained from "micro-economic" data (Theil, 1954). The problem of relations between "personal" and "unit" data has arisen in still another context, that of the analysis of information collected in opinion surveys (Kendall and Lazarsfeld, 1955). It has been pointed out (Duncan, 1959a) that the problem of individual vs. areal correlations is present in only slightly different form in the problem of whether relationships based on areal units of one order (e.g., counties) are consistent with relationships based on areal units of another order (e.g., states). In fact, the "aggregation problem" is an inescapable one in all statistical geography, and appears in various guises. As treated, for example, by McCarty, Hook, and Knos (1956, p. 16), it comes down to the problem of "scale," or more descriptively, to the problem of "areal levels of generalization." Their conclusion is a rather pessimistic one: "conclusions derived from studies made at one scale should not be expected to apply to problems whose data are expressed at other scales." Similarly, Robinson concluded that what he called "ecological correlations" could never be made to substitute for individual correlations. By contrast, Theil indicated conditions under which the "aggregation problem" might be resolved, and Goodman (1953) and Duncan and Davis (1953) showed that under favorable circumstances areal data could be used to estimate relationships at the individual level.

The other type of issue concerning statistical inference has to do with the applicability of significance tests and confidence interval estimation procedures to such statistics as coefficients of correlation or regression based on areal data. An early critic of ecological studies in sociology (Stephan, 1934) pointed out that neighboring areal units generally are more alike than are widely separated ones. (Note the analogy with autocorrelation in time series, as treated by R. L. Anderson, 1954.) Hence, conventional tests of significance could not rigorously be applied to measures of relationship derived from areal data. Pertinent fragmentary evidence on this point was presented by Duncan and Duncan (1957, Appendix H), in connection with studies of population and housing characteristics of urban neighborhoods. The same problem came up in investigations of weather-crop hypotheses, where investigators sought to test hypotheses by taking data from different locations as well as different years (Sanderson, 1954, p. 211). The problem has also been called to the attention of biological scientists. In the biometric literature one finds the important point that "the sampling theory of stationary processes in space is not completely analogous to the well-established theory of stationary time series, due to the fact that the variate of a time series is influenced only by past values, while for a spatial process the dependence extends in all directions" (Whittle, 1954; quotation from abstract). The use of "spatial lags" in a study of technological change by Griliches (1957) and the development of the "contiguity ratio" by Geary (1954) suggest that a breakthrough to a solution of this problem may be imminent.

On the basis of the foregoing discussion, it seems justifiable to conclude that investigators working with areal data in quite different disciplines find themselves in quite similar predicaments in respect to problems of measurement and inference. The evidence is even more clear that different disciplines share common methodological problems on the basis of like interests in particular substantive problems. We turn to some examples of such convergence.

The organization of a Regional Science Association, to which reference was made earlier, provides one ready example of convergence. Although the notion of an integrated "regional science" (Isard, 1956) may still be regarded as somewhat visionary, it is true that workers in several disciplines have seized on the "region" concept and have begun to manifest concern with regional problems in recent years. Among empirically oriented economists there is an increasing concern with regional aspects of economic fluctuations and economic growth (e.g., Vining, 1949; Perloff,

1957; Hanna, 1957b). In demography, Bogue (1950, 1954, 1959b) places heavy reliance on a proposed scheme for regional classification of population data. His approach traces back in part to the older school of "regional sociology"—which itself had given rise to significant methodological developments in statistical geography (e.g., Hagood, 1943)—and may be said to represent an attempt to systematize the techniques and premises of that school. Much of the recent work on regionalism borrows more or less directly from the longer tradition of "regional geography" (see summaries by Hartshorne, 1949; James and Jones, 1954, Chapter 2).

Regionalists of any disciplinary persuasion who propose to work systematically with quantitative data face some basic methodological questions. What criteria for regional groupings of areal units are to be accepted? What techniques can be used to meet these criteria? Given that even the most highly homogenized regions include intraregion variability, to what degree can regional traits be said to characterize each of the elements making up a region or contained therein? Given that so-called regions differ in many respects and never on a single characteristic only, what interpretation is to be given to the putative regional effects indicated by techniques of multivariate statistical analysis? Some of these questions are taken up in later sections, where the documentation will make it apparent that methodological contributions on the problems of regionalism are coming from a variety of disciplines.

The analysis of urban residential areas is a second substantive problem the convergence of interests on which has occasioned the exchange of techniques and procedures among disciplines. Sociologists are inclined to label studies in this field as "human ecology," but perusal of a text which adopts the view of human ecology as essentially the study of the "spatial pattern of areas" in the city (Quinn, 1950) reveals that much of the pertinent literature was produced by land economists, real estate analysts, criminologists, geographers, and others not identified as human ecologists. For a number of years the American Statistical Association has provided for annual meetings of specialists in the use of census tract statistics. These meetings have brought under one roof investigators and administrators concerned with such matters as "studies of disease, city planning, marketing analysis, labor market studies, civil defense, church planning, studies of juvenile delinquency, housing problems" and "retailing"—to cite a list presented in a recent publication on census tracts (United States Bureau of the Census, 1958, pp. 4-5). Political scientists have found use for census tract statistics and methods of urban analysis applied thereto in their studies of voting (e.g., Gosnell and Schmidt, 1936), and even psychologists have found the classification of urban areas by elaborate techniques an interesting exercise (Tryon, 1955). Foley (1953) gives a lengthy list of census tract studies.

We give but one more example of multi-disciplinary convergence on a particular class of problems—that of describing and accounting for the pattern of spatial movements or flows. From the time of Ravenstein (1885-89), at least, demographers have been interested in generalized patterns or models of flow phenomena. Systematic analyses have been made of the volume of movement as a function of distance (Bogue and Thompson, 1949; Price, 1948). Of the various mathematical models produced by demographers, the one currently receiving most attention is that of Stouffer (1940) phrased in terms of "intervening opportunities" (Isbell, 1944; T. R. Anderson, 1955). The problem of flow analysis was approached independently by various workers identified with "social physics," notably Zipf (1946) and Stewart (1948). These investigators actually concentrated on routine and repetitive movements or flows, rather than on migration proper, but the distinction between the two types of movement has not been consistently maintained in studies in this field. Probably the most active current interest in studying movement by these methods is that of the Swedish school of human geographers (Hannerberg *et al.*, 1957), but workers identified with "regional science" have recently become quite interested in their application to other sorts of problems (Carrothers, 1956).

## 1.2. Perspectives on Areal Differentiation

Let us now attempt a rather more general and inclusive classification of the points of view from which statistical geography is being developed. We must preface this presentation with a caveat, for experience suggests that any identification of significant differences of emphasis among scholars in their approaches to a shared body of techniques or subject matter is likely to carry a burden of unintended invidious connotations. We do not wish to exaggerate the dissimilarities among the frames of reference used in studies of areal differentiation or to imply that use of one precludes attention to others. If this point is kept clearly in mind, it will be worthwhile to indicate some relatively distinct sets of premises and objectives that may be discerned within the literature presenting quantitative investigations of areal data.

The classical interest of the geographer in areal differentiation merits first mention—on grounds of historical priority if no other. In a volume expounding *The Spirit and Purpose of Geography*, Wooldridge and East (1951, p. 28) express this interest as follows,

There can be no doubt that what interests the professional

geographer and the layman, as geographer, on their travels is
the essential pattern and quality of the earth's surface—"places"
or "areas" and the great difference between them. In its simplest
essence the geographical problem is how and why does one part
of the earth's surface differ from another.

We identify the preoccupation with how and why parts of the
earth's surface differ one from the other as the "classical interest
of the geographer" rather than as the whole of geography. This is
to recognize that geography—as is true of any discipline—is
made up of what geographers actually do, and geographers actually do a good many things that are not adequately encompassed
by any statement of the "simplest essence of the geographical
problem." We need not decide here whether methodologically
more sophisticated statements of the scope and concerns of
geography (e.g., Ackerman, 1958) in effect change the basic
orientation of the geographer or whether they only amplify the
implications of its statement. Clearly, individual geographers—
whatever may be the trend of their discipline—are interested in
and are making contributions to the study of areal differentiation
along lines more readily identified with the interests described
below than with the "classical" one. Significantly, these contributions are coming largely from those who are interested in "statistical geography" and who are dissatisfied with the level of rigor of
inferences based solely on maps—the mainstay of the "classical"
geographer.

A second type of orientation is suggested by the following
statement of an ecologist (Dice, 1952, p. 25),

> More adequate descriptions of the communities of all parts of the
> world are greatly needed. Quantitative measurements of the pop-
> ulation density of each component species and of the distribution
> of the individual organisms over each ecosystem are especially
> desirable.

Here the key term is "distribution," for what typifies this interest is the objective of describing how units of a given class (e.g., the organisms making up a species) are distributed over space. We need not look for obscure or esoteric reasons for the ecologist's interest in distribution; at least some of them are obvious. The range and pattern of a distribution provide immediate clues to the limits of tolerable environmental variation for an organism. Population growth and genetic processes differ according as the population is dense and highly aggregated or sparse and scattered. Associations between distributions of unlike species may suggest or test hypotheses concerning symbiotic or competitive relationships between them. Of course, not only the bioecologist is interested in distribution. The description of distributions has consumed much of the time of human ecologists from the inception of that discipline. Empirically oriented students of location economics similarly have given the matter much attention, and it would not be difficult to cite yet other substantive problems leading to a methodological concern with the measurement of distributions.

Interest in areal distributions merges more or less imperceptibly into a concern with the "spatial structure" of communities, economies, and societies. At the present time it is difficult to appreciate the magnitude of the effort which was required to establish the concept of an economy or a society as a territorially organized system. Nor is it easy to point to particular individuals responsible for bringing this notion into explicit and heuristic form. In economics, the pioneer usually mentioned is von Thünen. Durkheim and the French school of "social morphology" (see Halbwachs, 1960) together with developments stemming from Park's (1952) proposals concerning "human ecology" were certainly influential in sociology. It did not, of course, require the insights of such theorists to produce an awareness that social and economic activities are areally differentiated—the observation that people do different things and act differently in different places is as old as the "classical" interest of the geographer. But superficial observation may suggest only that, as under "primitive" conditions, such differentiation reflects differences in local habitats and in the historical antecedents of present "cultural" distinctions. The crucial point—which did require some extraordinary cogitation to make explicit—is that at least in modern societies and advanced economies areal differentiation of activities—division of labor on a territorial basis—is a basic structural principle and not an adventitious outcome of historical accidents. As we shall have occasion to point out, by no means all of the methodological implications of the view of socio-economic systems as spatial structures have yet become clear.

The gist of the attitude toward areal differentiation which we want to identify next is aptly expressed and illustrated in the following statements (Weatherford, 1957, p. 20 and p. 1),

> . . . farm wages follow a definite geographic pattern which has been quite stable for nearly a century, keeping its essential configuration through the fluctuations of the seasons and cycles. It is highly unlikely that such a regular and persistent pattern is the result of chance factors; almost surely there are basic logical reasons underlying the phenomenon. . . . Such a remarkable phenomenon calls for explanation.

The research ensuing from these observations amounts to a study in the "explanation of areal variation" in the phenomenon which interests the investigator—in this example, agricultural wages. In like fashion, research workers in each of the social sciences may find their attention drawn to "geographic patterns" and set about the construction of explanatory models to account for the observed areal variation. Note that the "classical" interest of the geographer has been inverted. The question is no longer, "Why do areas differ one from the other?" but, "Why does a particular variable—one warranting attention because of its relevance to a body of systematic theory—manifest variation from one place to another?"

We must acknowledge, finally, that a large proportion of any and all social and economic information is collected and tabulated on some kind of areal basis, and that by no means all investigators making use of such data are interested in areal or spatial problems as such. In some instances it is quite clear that areal differentiation is of interest only because it is assumed to reflect variation in the presumed causal factors which are actually the focus of interest. An illuminating illustration of how this may come about is furnished by the following bit of history (Sanderson, 1954, pp. 210-11),

> Weather-crop relationships at first were studied exclusively on the basis of time series of yields and weather factors for the same area or experimental plot. More recently, there has been a shift away from the analysis of time series of single stations or regions, substituting for it the analysis of partly spatial, partly chronological series, by pooling several years' data from locations in different parts of the country. This approach has the distinct advantage that one does not have to await the accumulation of a long series of data before an analysis is possible. The number of observations can be multiplied almost at will.

Here it is evident that the investigator deals with areal differentiation only because he can thereby collect observations varying with respect to the experimental variables (here, weather) whose effects he wishes to assess. Most instructive, incidentally, is the suggestion that this procedure is not wholly free from complications; Sanderson (1954, p. 211) notes,

> Information which can be obtained from the different items of a spatial series is not equivalent to the information which is available from the same number of annual observations. This is due to

the high degree of intercorrelation between weather conditions in adjacent regions. This similarity of meteorological conditions limits the amount of information that can be extracted from additional experimental plots in a given region or country.

The investigator who undertakes to analyze areal data for reasons extrinsic to their areal pattern is thus well advised to have some notion of the pitfalls to which this procedure is subject.

We have now identified the following "perspectives on areal differentiation": (a) chorographic interest in areal differentiation, i.e., in the characteristics of areas; (b) interest in areal distribution; (c) interest in spatial structure; and (d) concern with the explanation of areal variation. To these "perspectives" must be added (e) the use of areal data for objectives not intrinsically related to areal differentiation or spatial pattern. Though subtle and frequently blurred in actual research, the distinctions among these perspectives are not unimportant. Oftentimes they are manifested more clearly in respect to the ultimate objectives of research and the interpretation of research results than in the analytical operations employed in research. Yet insofar as these objectives govern the choice of problems, selection of data, and decisions concerning analytical procedures, they may have an important bearing on the direction taken by research. It seems worthwhile, therefore, to review the characteristics of these perspectives in a little more detail, for sake of clarification if not of emphasis.

Let us begin with a fuller description of the chorographic point of view. Hartshorne (1949, pp. viii-ix) states,

> The concept of geography as the study of the areal differentiation of the earth surface is justified in common sense by the well-known fact that things are different in different areas of the world and that these variations are somehow causally related to each other. There is a constant need, both in intellectual thought and for practical purposes, to know and understand what these differ-

ences are and how they are related, in order to understand the character of different areas.

The same authority (pp. 397-98) indicates that,

> . . . all geographical knowledge . . . may be organized according to the two different points of view required in studying the areal differentiation of the world: the view of any particular variable phenomenon in the relations of its differentiation to that of other variables all over the world, and the view of the total character of all the variables within the area.
>
> The organization of geographic knowledge in terms of the individual phenomena studied is called . . . "systematic geography" in this country. The organization according to areas is most commonly referred to as "regional geography."

Moreover, a careful distinction is made between the interests of the "systematic sciences" and those of "systematic geography" (Hartshorne, 1949, pp. 424-25),

> The distinction is in the point of view: that of the systematic science is focussed on the particular phenomena, which are studied in terms of distribution; that of systematic geography on the part which that distribution plays in forming areal differentiation. . . . *Ideally,* systematic geography receives from other sciences, or from general statistical sources, the necessary data concerning the distribution of any phenomenon. . . . Further, ideally, it receives from the systematic sciences the explanation of the distribution of the phenomenon. . . .

The point requiring emphasis here is that geography, viewed as a chorographic discipline, is concerned with the "areal differentiation *of the earth surface*"; it seeks to "understand the character of different *areas*"; and it is concerned with the distribution of particular phenomena only in terms of "the part which that distribution plays in forming areal differentiation." It is clear that these statements are meant to leave plenty of scope for investigation of areal differentiation in the "systematic sciences" where the focus of interest is on the explanation of areal variation or on discovery of spatial relationships rather than on the "character of different areas."

We may, therefore, record the geographer's traditional chorographic concern with the "character of different areas" as one legitimate perspective on areal differentiation and set alongside it some significant perspectives characteristic of the "systematic sciences." As given earlier, these include (a) the locational or distributional approach; (b) interest in spatial structure; and (c) concern for explaining areal (including "regional") variation. It is less important to make absolutely clear-cut distinctions among these points of view than to bring out the fact that the perspective of the investigator conditions the selection of data and choice of analytical framework in studies of areal differentiation.

The locational or distributional viewpoint is based on the concept of a population of items or elements. A "population," as the term is used here, consists of a spatially delimited aggregate of items conforming to a given definition each item of which, in principle, may be assigned a definite location at a given point in time. (For an excellent discussion of the concept of "population," see Hawley, 1950, Chapter 5.) Inasmuch as each item is assumed to have a uniquely defined location, the population has a "distribution" in space consisting of the aggregate of individual locations. It is important to note that where the items are so numerous that it is inconvenient to specify their individual locations, the distribution usually is described in terms of an allocation of the items among areal units, i.e., subdivisions of the total space delimiting the population. The central problem in locational or distributional studies, then, is to describe and account for significant features of the distribution.

For example, one might be concerned with a "population"

of human individuals in the United States. The problem might be to explain the concentration of population in metropolitan areas. Or, assuming the concern is with a "population" of manufacturing establishments, the question might be posed: Which of the two industries, blast furnaces and textile mills, is more likely to locate near markets and why? Or given a "population" of retail stores, one might investigate which types of retail outlet are more likely to occupy central locations within cities.

Some of what the economist calls "location theory" deals with this order of problem (although those parts of location theory that deal with the locational equilibrium of the individual firm appear to involve a different set of considerations and, in particular, may take a given distribution for granted rather than seeking to account for it). Recognition of "population distribution" as a significant aspect of demographic analysis (see Duncan, 1957a) likewise suggests the importance assigned to this viewpoint on areal differentiation in at least some "systematic sciences."

The term "structure" suggests a pattern of interrelationships among distinguishable parts of an organized whole (cf. Hawley, 1950, p. 206). By "spatial structure," therefore, we mean the pattern which relationships among parts assume in space. Such a pattern is not described merely by giving the relative locations of the several types of part; the nature of the relationships between parts or classes of parts also must be specified. The research worker, for example, might be concerned with the pattern of relationships among constituent parts of a community or an economy. Relevant descriptions might be given in terms of interchange between areal units, rates of flow between sites of activity, networks of communication channels, or transportation routes linking parts of a spatially organized activity.

Much of the human ecologist's work on community structure consists of analyses of spatial patterns; significantly, he often is limited to data on static distributions from which he attempts to infer structural characteristics (Duncan, 1957b). The study of the spatial structure of the economy, as distinguished from the mere analysis of distributions and locational tendencies, is still in the pioneering stages (see Vining, 1953, 1955). Indeed, the analysis of areal differentiation from any point of view is probably the exception rather than the rule in economics, although the relative emphasis on areal differentiation and non-areal aggregative analysis is now shifting rapidly in favor of the former.

The third perspective on areal differentiation characteristic of the "systematic sciences" is that of areal variation in various phenomena. The concern here is with the variation of a class of phenomena in terms of the places where these phenomena appear. Much of the analysis of data depicting areal variation is in the form of description, or such descriptive generalization as is involved in grouping together areal units having similar characteristics with respect to a given phenomenon to form "homogeneous regions." "Explanation" of the areal variation of a phenomenon may require reference to the areal variation of correlated phenomena which, so to speak, constitute the "environment" of the given phenomenon.

To illustrate: The investigator may note that incomes are lower in the South than in the North and conclude that income level varies among areas or differs from "region" to "region." He might further investigate the correlation of income level with character of natural resources, population characteristics, and industrial composition; and he might also refer to specialization of roles in a spatial structure as a "cause" of the observed areal variation in income level.

The foregoing example calls for reiteration of a point already made: The several perspectives on areal differentiation—(a) the chorographic and (b) those of the "systematic sciences," namely, the distributional, that of spatial structure, and that of areal variation—are by no means unrelated. The same data may conceivably serve all four types of interest, with appropriate modifications of the framework within which they are analyzed. Moreover, what are explanatory principles for one viewpoint are from another viewpoint the results of analysis. (This was made explicit in Hartshorne's quoted statement on the relation between systematic geography and the "systematic sciences.")

Another kind of distinction among viewpoints cuts across the four perspectives that have just been described. This distinction concerns the attitude taken toward areal units. From one point of view areal units are merely instrumental devices for classifying areal data and facilitating their analysis. For example, Vining (1955, p. 166) states,

> . . . any particular set of sub-areas, appearing as patches upon our map, is only an expedient for the classification of data and the sub-areas in themselves are not fundamental components of the structure being studied. They are analogous to class intervals that may be used in the construction of a frequency distribution of observations made upon a continuous variable. Such intervals that may be used are expedients for the classification of the data and are not inherent in the nature of the phenomena being described.

By contrast, the investigator working with certain types of areal units, for example cities or nucleated settlements, may consider that their unit character is inherent and not imposed by the investigator; at the same time, he may concede that the determination of precise boundaries or limits for such units requires some exercise of judgment. Indeed, the research problem may be defined as that of discovering the appropriate boundaries or system of delimiting units. Many writers on "regions" appear to take the latter view of "regional" units, although the more sophisticated recent discussions of regionalism generally concede that "a region is not an object, either self-determined or nature-given" but is rather "an intellectual concept . . . created by the selection of certain features that are relevant to an areal interest or problem" (James and Jones, 1954, p. 30).

Whichever attitude is adopted, it has to be recognized that some techniques of manipulating areal data produce results which have meaning only in relation to the particular set of areal units on which the results are based; whereas alternative methods of analysis may permit conclusions which are essentially independent (except for errors of approximation) of the basic system of areal delimitation. There will be further discussion of this important distinction in section 3.2.

Another general observation pertains to all four of the previously identified perspectives on areal differentiation. In one way or another temporal considerations are likely to enter the analysis. This comes about in several ways: (a) Certain of the characteristics whose areal differentiation is under study may be in the nature of events occurring over time or the ratios of such events to some class of items exposed to the occurrence of the event. A simple example is the annual birth rate or death rate of a population. (b) As suggested in the discussion of spatial structure, in particular, an important kind of areal data comprises records of flows or movements from place to place or between areas. Such movements, of course, can only occur over intervals of time. (c) From any of the standpoints mentioned, there may be interest in change taking place over time—changes in the "character of areas," changes in distribution, changes in spatial structure, or changes in nature and degree of areal variation of a given phenomenon. It may even be the case that one wants to study changes in occurrence rates from period to period, changes in patterns of flow or movement, or changes in rate of change in areal characteristics. Therefore, any consideration of areal analysis must reckon with the time dimension. For some purposes the distinction between areal analysis and temporal analysis may virtually disappear—e.g., if an investigator groups areal units into "regions" on the basis of the volume or rate of flows between them, or on the basis of correlation between their changes in characteristics.

The final category of studies making use of areal data encompasses all those in which the use of areal data is incidental to an interest in something besides the areal variation or spatial pattern; the fact that the data are ordered or arranged by areal units is accidental. There has been a good deal of discussion concerning the logic of such studies in the sociology literature; this discussion was touched off by a critique of so-called "ecological correlation" methods. According to W. S. Robinson (1950, p. 351),

> In an *ecological correlation* the statistical object is a *group* of persons. The correlation between the percentage of the population which is Negro and the percentage of the population which is illiterate for the 48 states . . . is an ecological correlation. The thing described is the population of a state, and not a single individual. The variables are percentages, descriptive properties of groups, and not descriptive properties of individuals.

The author points out that large numbers of sociological studies employing ecological correlation have been published. Noteworthy among them are the studies of voting behavior in which the investigator is legally prohibited from learning how the individual casts his ballot but can obtain frequencies and percentages of the votes cast on candidates or issues for areal units like precincts, wards, and counties. Although he might prefer to match individual votes with individual characteristics, the best he can do is match voting proportions against aggregate characteristics of the populations in the small areas by which votes are officially tabulated. Robinson (1950, p. 352) then declares,

> In each study which uses ecological correlations, the obvious purpose is to discover something about the behavior of individuals. Ecological correlations are used simply because correlations between the properties of individuals are not available.

Commentators on Robinson's paper (Menzel, 1950; Goodman, 1953, 1959; Duncan and Davis, 1953; Duncan and Lieberson, 1959) have uniformly pointed out that Robinson overstated his point. Correlations in which the units of observation are areal units are by no means always computed merely as an inferior substitute for the theoretically preferable individual correlations, although this may well hold true of some of the voting studies. There are many kinds of "ecological correlation" which do not even have a counterpart in an individual correlation—including some reported in a study the statistical analysis of which is credited in part to Robinson himself (Birdsell, 1953). A minor objection to Robinson's statement is that it perpetrates a usage of the term "ecological" in a meaning that has no generic connection with ecology or human ecology (Duncan, 1959a).

It must be conceded that this category of studies is not always easy to distinguish from studies in which the explanation of areal variation is the primary objective. Indeed, Bogue (1959b p. 392) has presented a viewpoint which may be regarded as a compromise between the two; he writes,

> . . . it is evident that if a given attribute, characteristic, or condition is regarded as being a factor in population behavior, it may be incorporated into the research study in two ways. It may be introduced distributively, as a varying attribute of the areas, or

it may be introduced directly, as an attribute of the persons enumerated. In the latter case, it would be statistically manipulated by cross-classifying it with the population events. Hence, in some circumstances, there may be a choice of the way in which a variable is introduced. . . . Any research study must be a compromise between the degree of cross-classification and the size of the areal unit employed in a distributive analysis. The extent to which each approach should be emphasized will vary with the problem.

While this passage might suggest that the author regards the use of areal data only as an expedient forced upon the investigator by the limitations of the available cross-tabulations of individual characteristics, in other sections of his paper he makes it clear that areal variation is worthy of study in its own right. In a later section (3.4) we shall have occasion to note a close complementarity between the techniques typically employed by investigators using areal data to study associations between individual characteristics and techniques employed in studies where the explanation of areal variation requires reference to "compositional" attributes of areal units. A clearer understanding of the technical relationships between the two approaches may, we hope, obviate the necessity for controversy between their proponents.

## 1.3. Scope and Purpose of This Monograph

The foregoing discussion has clearly shown that many kinds of problems involve areal differentiation in one way or another. The purposes for which analyses of areal data are undertaken likewise are diverse. To such a diversity of purposes corresponds a multiplicity of analytical techniques. Some kinds of methodological problems are common to virtually all techniques, while others are encountered only in respect to a narrow category of techniques. Short of encyclopedic treatment, it would be impossible to identify all the methodological problems that are likely to arise. The list of topics treated is consequently quite selective. The discussion is explicitly circumscribed in three respects: First, the chorographic perspective, with its characteristic emphasis on cartographic techniques, is bypassed for the most part. Second, attention is focussed on the kinds of quantitative areal data likely to be pertinent to demographic, sociological, and economic studies of areal differentiation, to the neglect of information not amenable to statistical manipulation and to the neglect of data likely to be only tangentially relevant to the indicated types of research. Third, there is no exposition of principles of statistical method as such; those pertinent to the discussion are assumed to be known to the reader.

Emphasis has been placed on the substantive variety of problems covered by our rubric, "statistical geography." These problems also spread over quite a range of conceptual and mathematical complexity. Some of the simplest questions that can be addressed to areal data may harbor unsuspected difficulties and thus may afford suitable pretexts for methodological discussion. Suppose, for example, that a research design calls for comparing the population densities of two (or more) communities. In section 2.1 it is shown that such a comparison is indeterminate in the absence of a specification of the areal units for which densities are to be computed. Furthermore, alternative, perhaps equally attractive, bases of comparison may give contrary results. While satisfactory pragmatic solutions may be found in particular instances of the kind described, it is important to realize that the same generic problem carries over into various kinds of measures of distributions (section 3.2). As the problem becomes more complicated and as the number of steps required for an analysis lengthens, it becomes all the more important to make explicit the assumptions on which the analysis proceeds.

To take an example from the other end of the complexity scale, suppose that the problem is that of ascertaining the "causes" of areal variation in such a phenomenon as levels of living. Since statistical analysis alone does not identify "causes," the investigator must face at the outset the problem of choosing a suitable analytical model for testing hypotheses based on a theory of causation. If, for whatever reason, the model chosen is linear regression, calculated over areal units at a given time, he might well find (as did the study by Duncan and Cuzzort, 1958) that farm levels of living vary among State economic areas in rather close association with degree of farm mechanization, as indicated by a correlation coefficient of around 0.8. However, if the analytical mode requires examination of concomitant changes in the dependent variable and the explanatory variable, the conclusion might be quite different. In the study just mentioned, the correlation between changes in levels of living and changes in mechanization was essentially nil. Reasons for such discrepancies between cross-sectional and longitudinal results are examined in section 3.6, where there is also a discussion of the related problem of choosing measures of change.

It is hoped that this brief allusion to two kinds of problem to be discussed in the sequel will give the reader some clue as to the kind of issues treated. He should be warned at the outset that many of these issues are not resolved in any final manner, and for some of them it is possible only to suggest possible leads for further methodological investigation. The monograph, then, is not a textbook or manual of recommended procedures. On the contrary, emphasis is placed on the identification of problems which seemingly need to be solved before such a textbook can be written.

The remainder of the book falls into two major parts. In the immediately following sections there is presented a somewhat detailed examination of the ways in which areal data are generated. Special mention is made of features of areal data that may occasion or require types of statistical analysis other than those commonly employed, for instance, in biometrics or survey analysis. Attention also is called to some special problems concerning the quality of areal data.

The remaining sections of the book are concerned with questions arising in the actual manipulation of quantitative areal data by statistical methods. The discussion is organized, in part, in terms of the distinctions made above among the perspectives on areal differentiation. Separate sections are devoted to the crucial "contiguity" problem and to problems arising in studying changes revealed by areal data.

The bibliography which concludes the volume is made up primarily of items to which reference is made in the text. It is by no means an exhaustive list of worthwhile readings dealing with the matters treated here, but it does furnish a good starting point for the reader who may wish to study certain questions more intensively or to broaden his acquaintance with the methodological literature of statistical geography.

# CHAPTER 2

# AREAL UNITS
# AND AREAL DATA

... all new sciences must traverse a wide territory of natural history before useful measurements can be made or fruitful hypotheses based
on them can be tested.

*—Lancelot Hogben*

IN interpreting the results obtained from analyses of areal data,
the investigator must be cognizant of certain of their characteristics, including the units by which they are compiled. Some major
characteristics of areal data that may affect the conclusions drawn
from areal analyses are outlined in this section. Their relevance
will become apparent in the subsequent discussion of techniques
for analyzing areal data.

## 2.1. Areal Units

For the most part, our discussion is limited to the case where
some "universe of territory" constitutes the field of study and this
universe is subdivided into a "basic set of areal units" on the condition that the subdivision exhausts the universe of territory and
no areal unit overlaps another. Both of the emphasized terms
pertain to the conditions of a particular problem. In one problem

the universe of territory might consist of the continental United States and the basic set of areal units might be the system of State economic areas used by the Bureau of the Census (see Bogue, 1951). In another problem, the universe might consist of the New England States, with counties as the basic areal units. The term "basic" identifies that set of areal units affording the finest subdivision of a territory, as distinguished from other sets which might be produced by combining members of the basic set. The units in the basic set, therefore, are the smallest ones, on the average, used in a given analysis.

In a complex study, one phase of the investigation may utilize a given basic set of areal units, whereas another phase will employ an alternative set. However, certain difficulties obtain in such a situation. One major problem—differences in size of areal unit—is discussed in section 3.4.

Statistical data collected directly by the investigator can be compiled by a set of areal units delimited expressly for purposes of his analysis. In many studies, however, the investigator must depend upon official sources for statistical information. The data collected and compiled by official agencies usually are presented for political or administrative units, such as minor civil divisions, counties, or States. On occasion, such statistics are given for units delimited primarily for statistical purposes, such as census tracts within major cities or State Economic Areas within States. Whatever the areal breakdown of the data, however, it is the rule rather than the exception that the set of areal units was devised for purposes other than the specific ones of the investigator. Areal units are, therefore, likely to differ not only in the characteristic whose variation is the focus of study but also in characteristics which may constitute "disturbing" factors of one sort or another. Illustratively, most systems of areal units in official statistics include units differing in size and in number of inhabitants. The investigator may want to control or take account of variation in these characteristics; and consequently, he may effect a standardization by expressing land use categories as proportions of total land surface or computing per capita ratios for analytical purposes.

However, it is not always possible to effect a suitable standardization. Inter-area comparison of internal migration rates is a case in point. A "migrant" usually is defined as an individual who moves across the boundary of an areal unit within a specified time period. Clearly, other things being equal, the rate of out-migration (number of persons leaving the area divided by number of persons residing in the area) will be greater for small areal units than for large areal units (see Bogue, 1959a). Conceivably, if one could assume that the propensity to move, i.e., probability of moving, a given distance, $p(d)$, were constant for each individual in the population, and if a simple assumption about the distribution of population within areal units were accepted, an "expected" amount of out-migration could be ascertained by calculating the proportion of moves carrying a mover across the boundary of an areal unit. Expression of actual out-migration as a deviation from "expected" out-migration, then, might be regarded as a measure of out-migration standardized for size of areal unit. The problem is further complicated by the fact that for areas of the same size out-migration rates would be higher for a long and narrow areal unit than for a circular one. Students of internal migration for the most part have had to content themselves with making informal allowance for the non-comparability of migration rates arising from differences in the size and shape of areal units; however, for a sophisticated version of the above mentioned probability approach see Kulldorff (1955).

Additional emphasis may be given the problem of size of areal unit by considering the selection of an appropriate areal unit for studying variation in population density over a territory. Whereas the concept of density is perfectly clear in respect to any specified unit of area, as soon as one is at liberty to select an areal unit for the calculation of density, he can manipulate, within limits, the result obtained. An example in the nature of a *reductio ad absurdum* is shown in Table 1. Given the problem of determining the density of population in the "vicinity" of 31st Street and Indiana Avenue in Chicago, among the infinity of alternative solutions of the problem are the nine shown in the table, ranging from 50.7 to 91,300 persons per square mile. Or, to consider

## Table 1
### Illustrative Population Densities for Various Areal Units: 1950

| Areal unit | Land area (Square miles) | Density (Population per sq. mi.) |
|---|---|---|
| Chicago, census tract #550 | 0.024 | 91,300 |
| Chicago, community area #35 | 1.623 | 48,500 |
| Chicago, city | 207.5 | 17,450 |
| Chicago, urbanized area | 638.0 | 7,713 |
| Chicago, metropolitan district | 1,184.2 | 4,283 |
| Chicago, Standard Metropolitan Area | 3,617 | 1,519 |
| Economic subregion #64 | 7,328 | 958.7 |
| East North Central division | 244,867 | 124.1 |
| Continental United States | 2,974,726 | 50.7 |

what may seem to be a more reasonable problem, suppose one wished to ascertain whether the density of Detroit was greater or less than that of Chicago in 1950. Some readily available answers are as follows:

| Areal unit | Detroit Density (Population per sq. mi.) | Detroit/Chicago (Ratio) |
|---|---|---|
| City | 13,249 | 0.76 |
| Urbanized area | 6,734 | 0.87 |
| Metropolitan district | 3,375 | 0.79 |
| Standard Metropolitan Area | 1,535 | 1.01 |

Clearly, the result of a density comparison between the areal units is not independent of the specifications for the boundaries of the areal units. The inescapable margin of indeterminacy in density comparisons is a consequence of the mathematical character of the ratio: population/area. The ratio is defined only for non-zero area, and does not necessarily approach a unique limit as size of areal unit approaches zero. If one reckons that a standing man occupies a square foot of land, then "standing room only" is equivalent to a density of 27,878,400 persons per square mile, a density perhaps locally approximated in ephemeral crowds. Under most circumstances, a standing man is surrounded by at least a small area having zero density. The discontinuity of the distribution of population over space has the following consequence. Taking any arbitrary grid of areal unit boundaries and moving it haphazardly over a territory whose population is not uniformly spaced produces fluctuations in the density of each cell of the grid. By shifting the grid one could maximize the grid-cell density in the vicinity of a specified point, but the density of any other cell would then vary in an unpredictable manner. Hence, under conditions that may differ rather widely, the densities of any two cells cannot be strictly comparable. It has to be recognized that any set of areal unit boundaries is essentially arbitrary from this standpoint. Consequently, when one computes the density of an areal unit, he obtains a figure which, though well defined, is necessarily relative to areal boundaries and hence fictitious in a sense. The same is true of the calculation of density isopleth lines, sometimes used by geographers to represent population distribution.

Another important respect in which the use of areal data may require the investigator to proceed on the basis of assumptions which are essentially fictitious concerns the "homogeneity" of areas. Hartshorne (1949; pp. xiv, 439) makes the following observation on methods of study in regional geography,

> In order to comprehend the actual interrelations of phenomena in specific places it is necessary to consider small subdivisions ["chores"] within each of which the local variations of the various factors are arbitrarily ignored. . . . in any finite area, however small, the geographer is faced with an interrelated complex of factors, including many semi-independent factors, all of which vary from point to point in the area with variations only partially dependent on each other. He cannot integrate these together except by arbitrarily ignoring variations within small units of area, i.e., by assuming uniform conditions throughout each small, but finite unit.

Thus the assumption that the "chore" (the term is equivalent here to "basic areal unit") is homogeneous is necessarily false. If it were possible to measure degree of homogeneity, it doubtless would be found that homogeneity is directly related to average size of "chores," but this relationship could not be mathematically determinate, inasmuch as not only size of "chore," but also the location of boundaries affect its homogeneity.

The question of how much departure from homogeneity is tolerable in terms of the purposes of a specific investigation has seldom been posed in a way that would admit of objective solution. However, it is sometimes possible to obtain empirical findings that are relatively insensitive to variation in homogeneity of areal units (Duncan and Duncan, 1955a). Much effort has been expended in devising systems of areal units in which the units are thought to be suitably homogeneous, but criteria for adjudging a "suitable" degree of homogeneity have not been elaborated (e.g., Bogue, 1951; J. Smith, 1954; Myers, 1954). There has probably been too much of a tendency to think of homogeneity as a purely methodological problem; investigators need to strengthen the theories that lead them to expect homogeneity or lack thereof (Hawley and Duncan, 1957). The studies of Kish (1954) and Varley (1956) provide significant examples of a kind of thinking that should be followed up.

The extent to which the use of theoretically justifiable substantive assumptions may overcome the methodological indeterminacy of data on areal units is a moot question. For example, one might compute densities for areal units believed to have a "functional unity," rather than representing arbitrarily demarcated segments of space. Or, one might argue that within a sufficiently small "chore," although it exhibits internal heterogeneity, each individual experiences essentially the "same" environmental conditions. This type of argument, from the standpoint of the individual and his perceptions of the environment, is offered by Tryon (1955, p. 4). Quite clearly the terms of any such arguments would differ from one investigation to another; consequently a general methodological solution for the problem of indeterminacy in comparisons of areal units is unlikely to emerge from such arguments.

## 2.2. Types of Areal Data

Though it is not feasible in this essay to list all the kinds of areal data that might be used in one investigation or another, some formal properties of certain of the major types of data employed in areal analyses can be identified. These types are first described briefly and then are discussed more fully in the indicated sections.

(a) If the universe of territory under study is regarded as containing a population of items, then the areal units into which the territory is divided may be regarded as, among other things, collections, or subpopulations, of such items. Examples of items making up areally delimited collections are inhabitants, labor-force members, families, dwelling units, farms, business establishments, churches, nucleated settlements, and so on. A problem with usually minor but sometimes significant consequences is that items cannot always be unambiguously assigned to an areal unit. For example, a farm may lie in two counties; a man may reside in one city and work in another; a birth may occur in one State to a couple living in another State. Ordinarily, close study of the situation will suggest suitable rules for disposing of the majority of such cases. However, if each item itself has an areal extent that is large compared to the areal unit supposed to contain it, it may be difficult to formulate a wholly satisfactory rule (e.g., one for allocating to individual counties the cities whose limits extend over two or more counties). (See section 2.3.)

(b) An areal unit regarded as a segment of space has an area, i.e., a spatial size. Moreover, the unit's total area may be composed of areas of various kinds. Thus data of this type may indicate the amount or proportion of the land surface of an areal unit which falls into various categories of land use, soil type, topography, vegetational cover, etc. (See section 2.4.)

(c) An areal unit may be treated as a site for phenomena located within it. Such phenomena may be considered zero-, one-, or two-dimensional, according to the convention used in describing them—it is, after all, a convention that allows us to neglect the fact that all phenomena on the earth's surface take up volume, i.e., have three dimensions (James, 1958, p. 24). Thus a sufficiently small feature, such as a weather observation station, may be thought of as located at a point within the areal unit, though in actuality it takes up space. Features like rivers, roads, or railroads, when the areal units in which they are located are comparatively large, may be regarded as essentially "linear" phenomena. It may, however, be pertinent to consider the amount of space they take up, that is, their area, in addition to their linear pattern. Should it be necessary to take into account the areal extent of locations—e.g., the location of urban settlements within a small areal unit—this type of data resembles the preceding (areal unit as a segment of space). (See section 2.5.)

(d) Certain types of data on an areal unit explicitly and intrinsically involve comparison with other areal units in the set of areal units. For example, the observation that Iowa is the tenth ranking State with respect to some variable implies a comparison between Iowa and each other State. (See section 2.6.)

(e) The final type of data to be mentioned includes those which characterize the "location" of the areal unit in terms of other units or in terms of the entire territory, as well as other types of inter-unit relationships. For example, one might describe the location of an areal unit by giving the distance and direction of its geographic center from the national capital. The region in which the areal unit is located might be specified. One can devise indexes of the accessibility of an areal unit to the site of a resource located elsewhere in the territory, or classify areal units according to whether they lie on routes connecting major cities. Aside from such positional data, inter-unit relationships may be observed in terms of exchanges of population through migration, relative status in a hierarchy of governmental units, or location in one unit of activities controlled from headquarters in another, as a few examples. In all data of this type, the essential factor is that observations on a given areal unit depend on the context of the remainder of the territory; the unit cannot be described as though it existed in isolation. (See section 2.7.)

Consideration of kinds of data that result from combining data of two or more of the foregoing types would lengthen the list substantially. A simple example is the ratio of population to area; it relates information on the areal unit as a collection of items (people) to information on the areal unit as a segment of two-dimensional space. A datum like the proportion of farm houses located on paved roads involves the characterization of the unit in terms of the relation of a collection of items to a linear site feature of the areal unit.

## 2.3. Areal Unit as a Collection of Items

Most problems involved in analyzing data in this form arise from the fact that grouping items by areas is a form of aggregation, and the aggregated data are what have to be manipulated. Seldom is the investigator interested solely in the number of items in each areal unit. He also wishes to use information on their characteristics and the relationships in which they are involved. If several types of characteristics are to be considered simultaneously, the analysis becomes quite complex. It seems worthwhile, therefore, to consider some of the ways in which unit data are formed from data on the items contained in the unit. (The discussion of "personal" and "unit" data by Kendall and Lazarsfeld, 1955, is helpful in this connection.) The relevance of these considerations to problems of manipulating areal data will be indicated subsequently (Chapter 3). The presentation is made more concrete, without loss of generality, by supposing that the items contained in an areal unit are people; much the same discussion could be given for populations of other kinds.

For each individual in the areal unit, certain kinds of data can be obtained which do not depend logically on his membership in that unit. These may be conveniently classified as follows (see also Coombs, 1953): (a) category of an attribute (sometimes called a "qualitative variable") which may be dichotomous (as sex) or manifold (as nativity), and unordered (as industry of employment) or ordered (as socio-economic status group); (b) value of a (quantitative) variable (as age, income, number of school years completed), which may be discrete or continuous, and may be measured on either an interval scale or a ratio scale. Provision must also be made (c) for observations on changes in the characteristics of individuals in the course of a specified time period, such as the change from single to married status, or from one occupation to another. The observation of "social mobility" (change of status or characteristic), of course, applies only to characteristics subject to change. Provision must likewise be made (d) for observations on entries to and exits from the population via birth and death (or on their counterparts such as entry into and retirement from the labor force).

Other kinds of observation made on an item belonging to an areal unit require explicit reference to the areal unit; these include (e) migration of individuals into or out of the areal unit; (f) observations in the form of a comparison between one individual and one or more others in the areal unit or a relationship between an individual and one or more other individuals in the areal unit; (g) observations in the form of a relationship of an individual to some aspect of the areal unit.

Now, an areal unit is being considered here as a "subpopulation" of the population of items included in the universe of territory which constitutes the field of study. It follows that data on this sub-population—the items "contained in" the areal unit—may be manipulated in any of the ways that population data may be manipulated. The point to bear in mind is that, as a consequence of such manipulations, one obtains a set of data for areal units, or unit data, only some of whose properties resemble those of the data on individual items in the population. For example, the average income of individuals in an areal unit can be treated as a datum on the unit (for some purposes) in much the same way that the individual income as a datum on the individual is treated. However, this areal datum can be handled like an individual datum only if certain of its properties are disregarded—e.g., there is a dispersion of incomes around the areal average, whereas there is no such dispersion around the income of an individual. (One can, of course, study the variation of an individual's income over a period of years around the average for the whole period, but the foregoing example pertains to a single year; introduction of temporal variation would complicate not only the individual but also the areal datum.) Furthermore, an areal datum like the birth rate of the population in the areal unit or the sex ratio of this population has no close analogy with any individual datum. It is well, therefore, to consider some of the ways in which unit data are generated from individual data.

(a) The simplest datum—in the sense that it may be expressed as a single absolute number—on the areal sub-population is its size, i.e., the number of items included. Such a datum may be of interest in itself; for example, the investigator might compare more populous with less populous units. The datum on size is more often used in conjunction with some other datum to form (b) a ratio such as that of population size to area (population density) or the ratio of the size of one population to that of another class of items, e.g., number of inhabitants to number of retail stores.

Corresponding to individual characteristics in the form of

attributes and variables are areal data in the form of (c) frequency distributions of individual characteristics, and (d) statistics derived from these distributions. The distributions may be univariate, if only one characteristic is considered, or bivariate or multivariate if more than one is examined simultaneously in cross classification. The whole array of statistical methods for analyzing and summarizing distributions, therefore, may be brought into play. The important point is that the application of such methods to the sub-population of each areal unit in a set of units produces a set of data describing variation among areal units; for example: variation among areal units in respect to the proportion of the population classified as nonwhite; variation in respect to median number of school years completed; variation in respect to the concentration of income within each areal unit; variation in the degree of correlation within areal units between two individual characteristics; etc. Thus one may have for a set of areal units such unit data as proportions, averages, measures of dispersion, and measures of covariation.

Corresponding to the individual events mentioned earlier—social mobility (change of characteristic), birth and death, and in- or out-migration—are (e) rates for areal units. Such rates may be included with measures of frequency distributions among the characteristics of areal units which have no exact analogue among characteristics of individuals.

When observations on the individuals in an areal unit take the form of inter-individual comparisons, it may be difficult to specify a corresponding unit datum. For example, if the individuals in a county are ranked in order of income, there is a rectangular frequency distribution of the ranks, but this distribution conveys no information about the areal unit or its sub-population as such, since any areal unit likewise will have such a rectangular distribution.

(f) When individuals are characterized in terms of their relationships to other individuals in the sub-population, to members of a sub-population of another class, or to some aspect of the areal unit, there may or may not be a way to extract a meaningful unit datum from the aggregate of such relationships. Suppose, for example, that each farm household in a county is classified in terms of the trade center in which it purchases most of its clothing. To secure a meaningful areal datum, one would probably analyze this pattern of relationships by expressing it in terms of characteristics of the individual households. One could measure the distances from farms to the respective trade centers and regard "distance travelled to trade" as a characteristic of the household. Or one might classify each household according to whether its trade center is located in the same county or in a different county from the location of the farm; the corresponding areal datum would then be number or proportion of households trading within the county versus those trading outside the county. There are, of course, other devices for summarizing a pattern of inter-individual relationships to secure unit data, such as the various sociometric indices (see Proctor and Loomis, 1951). As in the case of ratios, rates, and measures of frequency distributions, such unit data lack exact analogues in individual data.

(g) From unit data of any of the preceding kinds secured at two or more points in time one can obtain measures of change in the characteristics of areal units. Because the measurement of change is discussed in detail in section 3.6, it is sufficient to note here that such incremental data may take a variety of forms.

The foregoing categories certainly do not exhaust the possibilities for forming areal unit data from observations on the individuals making up the population of an areal unit. It suffices to call attention to the fact that various involved manipulations of individual data produce unit data with distinctive properties. (h) For example, the computation of a net reproduction rate for an areal unit involves calculations based on the births occurring to women residing therein, classified by age of mother; on the female deaths, likewise age-specific; and on the female population by intervals of age. The reduction of this information to a single summary figure requires a fairly complex sequence of manipulations of the data. This category of areal unit data may, therefore, be referred to as complex "indexes" of one form or another. There is virtually no limit to the number of kinds of indexes that an investigator may devise.

In this section various relationships between observations on individuals and characterizations of the population which these individuals make up have been noted. As long as attention is confined to a single areal unit, the problems that come up are relatively familiar. But the circumstance that characteristics of areal units are themselves to be analyzed in terms of areal differentiation—differences in characteristics among areal units—means that a whole order of additional problems must be faced. The distinctions made in the foregoing discussion must be kept in mind in connection with the topic of Chapter 3, the analysis of areal data.

## 2.4. Areal Unit as a Segment of Space

Under this heading fall those data on areal units which result from the measurement of area or of some phenomenon in terms of the area or amount of space it covers. The primary datum is, of course, the size of the areal unit itself, measured in appropriate units such as acres or square miles. This datum is used as a base for ratios (e.g., population density) or as a total on which to percentage the distribution of area in various uses, with various types of cover, and the like.

The importance of taking account of area size in analyzing areal data has been pointed out (A. H. Robinson, 1956; p. 233),

> When the geographer attempts statistical analysis, and especially correlation of distributions having areal extent, he must in many instances modify the general statistical formulae in order to take into account his areal point of view. This generalization applies when the data with which one is working are averages, percentages, ratios, or densities distributed over area and localized by . . . areal units. . . . When the areal units to which the values relate are not the same size, as is unfortunately usually the case, significant discrepancies in size should be taken into account; otherwise the results of computations may be meaningless.

On the face of the matter, this statement would appear to have greatest force where the "averages, percentages, ratios, or densities" are themselves derived from area measurements. Thus it is clear that if one is computing the average proportion of land in farms for a set of counties, the average must be weighted by the total areas of the counties to make it the same as the proportion of land in farms for the entire universe of territory. However, it is not equally clear what area weights, if any, are appropriate when the areal data pertain to such things as the populations of the areal units. The issue raised here is one aspect of the problem of aggregation to which attention is given in section 3.1.

Frequently areal units are handled categorically by classifying each of them according to a prevailing or predominant phenomenon or condition that has areal expression. For example, areal units may be placed in categories of a classification scheme of types of climate or types of terrain. Areal units may be assigned to a type-of-farming category in terms of the predominant type of farming carried on therein; in this case, predominance may not even be determined on the basis of land use, but perhaps by production or value of products. In all such instances, it is clear that the categoric treatment of the areal unit is somewhat less precise than the calculation of the proportions of area characterized by various conditions. However, by the same token, it yields a datum for the areal unit that may be somewhat easier to manipulate in comparisons of areal units.

## 2.5. Areal Unit as a Site or Location

Description of the "features" situated in an areal unit may serve either to indicate the location of these features or to characterize the areal unit in which they are located. The precision of the location of a feature obtained by designating the areal unit in which it occurs depends on the size and shape of the areal unit. Moreover, characteristics of the areal unit may then be interpreted as characteristics of the location. For example, the location of a city may be given as a certain State, which has certain climatic, agricultural, and industrial characteristics. Enumeration, description, and measurement of features located in it provide important data on the areal unit. Thus counties may be classified according to whether they do or do not contain an urban place, or according to size of largest place located therein.

In both these ways of using location information, a "problem of relevance" is encountered. In the location of features, the problem may be that the areal unit is too large to afford a sufficiently precise indication of location. Or conditions prevailing in just a part of its area may be the really significant determinants or consequences of the location of a feature. Ordinarily, then, the investigator must assume that his information on the characteristics of the areal unit actually serves to describe the "context" of the location, but this assumption is always only approximately true at best. The same problem arises with respect to the use of features to characterize an areal unit. For example, the location of a city within a county may be a significant indicator of the accessibility of urban services to the rural residents of that county. However, it may happen that some rural residents live too far from the city to avail themselves of its services; or, on the other hand, residents of a county in which no city is located may actually have ready access to the facilities of a city in an adjacent county.

If a given set of areal units is evaluated as a coordinate system for specifying locations, the investigator must be on guard against various inadequacies which it may have for the purpose. The units may be too large on the average, so that they lack precision as locations. They may be too small, on the average, so that they fail to give "enough" of the context of the locational site. They may be so variable in size and/or shape that errors of either of these kinds are highly variable, thus ruling out the possibility of a simple allowance or correction for a constant error or narrow range of error. The geographer sees this as a problem of "scale" (for example, McCarty *et al.*, 1956).

## 2.6. Areal Unit as a Member of a Set of Areal Units

To this point, the discussion has concerned primarily those types of areal data in which an areal unit is observed with no explicit reference to characteristics of other areal units. There are cases, however, where it serves the purposes of an investigation to compare an areal unit with one or more others. For example, to describe a given areal unit as "below average" on a certain variable, one must have values of this variable for all areal units included in the set under study and compute the average of the variable over the set of units. It even seems advantageous in some cases to scale a variable with reference to its frequency distribution over the set of areal units. For example, the county farm-operator family level-of-living index prepared by the Agricultural Marketing Service is so scaled that the (unweighted) United States county average for 1945 equals 100 (Hagood *et al.*, 1957).

It is important to realize how the meaning of an areal datum involving comparisons of areal units depends on the attitude taken toward areal units. If the system of areal units is such that, for the purposes of a given investigation, each unit is assumed to be uniquely defined and substantively meaningful boundaries are given independent of the investigator's decisions, then a comparison of values of areal units is relatively unambiguous. For example, a definite meaning can be given the statement that Missouri ranks $n^{th}$ among the forty-eight States in per capita expenditures for public roads. In this case, States are not only areal units, they are units of political organization having the function of allocating public funds to highway construction.

Suppose, however, one wished to assert that a certain State Economic Area has a below average annual rainfall. Now, State Economic Areas are combinations of counties used for purposes of statistical tabulations and analyses. Although their delimitation was influenced by information on climate, this is but one element that entered into the determination of their boundaries. In any case, one would find it difficult to maintain that any set of areal units affords a "natural" and uniquely valid framework for comparisons of climate. Therefore, one must concede that the set of areal units represents a subdivision of the total territory which is more or less arbitrary from the standpoint of this problem. The position of a given areal unit in an array of areal units by amount of rainfall is in part a function of the way in which units were delimited. Suppose that in the arid parts of the country, "State Economic Areas" (SEA's) are relatively large on the average, whereas in humid parts they are relatively small. The unweighted average rainfall for all SEA's will then be higher than if the reverse were true. If an SEA were close to the average, it would be easy to shift its position, say, from below average to above average by subdividing several of the below-average SEA's, thus increasing the number of areal units with low rainfall and bringing down the average. This particular problem could be avoided by weighting the average by the size of areal unit (see A. H. Robinson's suggestion cited in section 2.4). However, it would still be difficult to interpret the magnitude of a given unit's departure from the average, because the frequency of deviations from the average would be a function of the relative number of units delimited in parts of the country with greatly different rainfall. These remarks apply, *a fortiori,* if the comparison of areal units is given in terms of ranks or quantiles.

Now if a datum on any areal unit, expressed as a comparison with other units, is ambiguous, the meaning of any statistic derived from a frequency distribution of characteristics of areal units is likewise equivocal. Note that we have not said that statements based on a frequency distribution of areal unit characteristics are meaningless. They do have empirical content, and they can be put to the test of evidence. What is at issue is the extent to which such statements reflect the arbitrary operations or decisions made by the investigator. Suppose a research worker computes per capita income for each county in the United States, arranges these per capita figures in a frequency distribution, and computes its mean and standard deviation (whether with weights or not). Presumably the mean will approximate the per capita income for the whole of the United States, and one would doubt-less get a fairly similar mean using areal units other than counties. However, the standard deviation—which depends on differences among areal units or inter-unit comparisons—will not be so readily interpreted. It is a genuine datum but one which, in some degree, represents the investigator's decision to work with counties—rather than, say, SEA's or States—at the same time that it represents a fact about areal variation in income. One can justly raise the question: Does the computation of the standard deviation of county per capita incomes really tell us something about income distribution? Does it represent a "fact" or an "artifact"? If it is at least something of the former, could we learn this "fact" without using this particular set of areal units, and, if not, how can we justify its use on grounds other than pure expediency?

The discussion will have to return to issues related to the foregoing, though these issues will by no means be resolved.

## 2.7. Areal Unit in Relation to Other Units

Two main types of data fall under this heading. First are observations on an areal unit that take the form of specifying its "position" or "location" with respect to other areal units or in the spatial context of the entire universe of territory. Second are data on inter-unit relationships.

A significant example of the first type of datum is the classification by Bogue (1949) of the counties in the United States in terms of metropolitan relationship. Each county was assigned to the nearest metropolitan center and its distance thereto was measured. Bogue's study then proceeded to examine levels of economic activity in counties in relation to size of metropolis, distance from the metropolis and certain other important locational parameters.

The characterization of an areal unit in terms of "population potential" is an illustration of an important class of areal data that depend on the unit's position in an areal distribution. In terms of its definition, the potential of population at a given point in a universe of territory is ascertained by measuring the distance of each individual from that point, computing the reciprocal of that distance, and summing those reciprocals. In practice, one must approximate the potential at a point by dividing the universe of territory into a manageable number of areal units, measuring the distance of the "center" of each unit to the given point, and employing the following formula:

$$\text{potential at a point} = \sum_{1}^{k} \frac{P_i}{D_i},$$

where $P_i$ is the population of the $i^{\text{th}}$ areal unit, $D_i$ is the distance of its center from the given point, and the summation is over all $k$ areal units. Having ascertained the population potential of a suitable number of points by direct computation, one may interpolate graphically for other points, or may construct a map showing isolines of population potential (i.e., interpolate graphically for the loci of points having equal potentials). Figure I is such a map constructed for the United States in 1950. Since the computation method is approximate, the detail and the reliability of the result depend on the number of areal units employed. Figure I is a fairly coarse grained potential map, although the areal breakdown on which it is based is somewhat more detailed than that employed in various potential maps which have previously been published. In particular, Figure I fails to show details accurately in the vicinity of large urban centers. As its definition indicates, the measurement of potential pertains strictly to points. Thus if one speaks of the potential of an areal unit, it must be

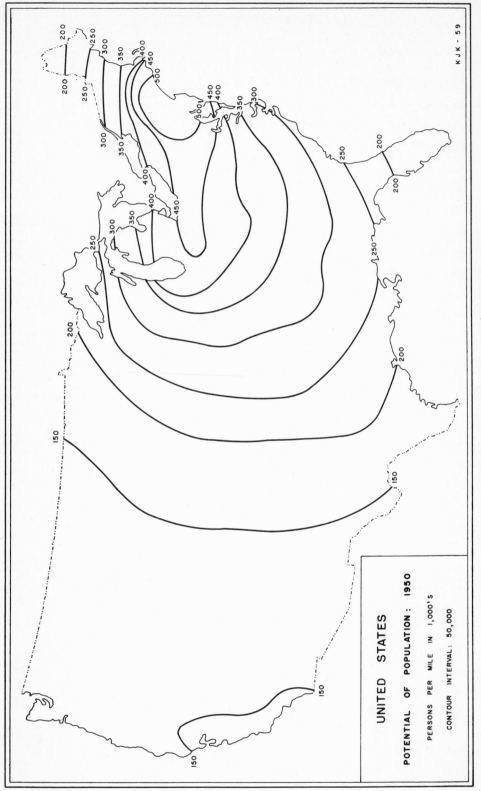

Figure I. Potential of Population, United States: 1950

in some average sense, or in terms of some "representative" point within the areal unit. However, the important matter for this discussion is not the character of the approximation involved in assigning a potential value to an areal unit. Rather, it is the fact that potential in an areal unit is a function of the distribution of population over the entire universe of territory of which the areal unit is a part. Thus, to measure the potential of an areal unit is to take into account its position within the universe of territory as well as its own size and number of inhabitants. (For further discussion of population potential and related matters, see Stewart, 1947; Harris, 1954; Duncan, 1957a, b.)

As a final example of a "positional" or "contextual" datum on an areal unit, we mention its location in a particular region. We defer consideration of the implications of the "region" concept to section 3.5. However, the term is used throughout this essay in the operational sense of a "grouping of contiguous areal units," with the set of such groupings constituting an exhaustive and mutually exclusive (not overlapping) classification of all areal units in the universe of territory. The region, then, is fundamentally a higher order areal unit formed as a combination of adjacent units from the basic set of areal units. To specify the regional location of an areal unit, therefore, is to indicate a collection of other areal units which is regarded as the "context" of the given areal unit. The issue of how much or what kind of information is conveyed by the statement that an areal unit falls in a certain region is a delicate one. In a sense, of course, regional location tells us "where" an areal unit is. Insofar as the investigator may be familiar with how things differ from one region to another, he may gain an impression of the character of an areal unit by ascertaining its regional location. But the main point here is that specification of an areal unit's membership in a regional grouping of units is a locational or positional datum that intrinsically involves reference to other areal units.

Data on inter-unit relationships form the other main type alluded to above. An obvious illustration is the figures on streams of migration collected in censuses. These may show, for example, the number of migrants originating in a given SEA who moved to another specified SEA. Quite similar, from a formal standpoint, are data on movements of commodities between States (e.g., Ullman, 1957). It is important to note that such data in simple origin-destination form do not as such supply information on the spatial orientation of movements or flows. However, their analysis almost invariably makes reference to the direction of movement or to the distance separating areal units involved in the interchange of population, goods, or the like. Cartographic presentation, of course, draws attention to distance and direction relationships of units involved in interchanges; and the statistical study of flows commonly employs distance explicitly as an explanatory or control variable.

Interchange of population or commodities is, of course, but one type of inter-unit relationship. It does not seem advisable to attempt a typology of such relationships here, but attention should be called to two things. First, there is an enormous variety of ways in which such relationships may be described, some of which may embody quite complex manipulations of data. One example is the interregional input-output table set forth by Isard (1951). Another description may be as simple as the observation that two areal units are served by the same major highway. Second, although data on inter-unit relationships may not make explicit reference to the spatial aspects of the relationships, these are likely to be an indispensable element of the framework within which the relationships are analyzed.

## 2.8. Quality of Areal Data

It is beyond the scope of this study to attempt an evaluation of all the various kinds of areal data that investigators employ. However, several typical problems of the quality of areal data warrant discussion in general terms, since they have important bearing on the design of research.

For many kinds of study, where the universe of territory is quite extensive, the collection and processing of data for studies of areal differentiation are beyond the competence of the individual investigator. Consequently, the availability of areal data depends heavily on the practices of government statistical offices and other agencies whose resources are allocated to these tasks. This means that the kind and quality of data available may bear no close relationship to the relative importance of different sorts of data in the context of a particular investigation. A frequent circumstance is that different series of data are available with differing degrees of areal breakdown. Therefore, the more complex the study design, in respect to number of variables to be analyzed, the smaller is the chance that all parts of the data will be sufficiently detailed in respect to the areal units for which they are compiled. This is especially likely to be true in connection with studies involving data for two or more points in time. It is, indeed, rare that comparable small-area data on a variety of variables can be assembled for any considerable number of time periods. (For illustrations of this problem, see Duncan, 1956.)

In investigations involving interrelations and changes of a number of variables, research workers are likely to find that a considerable proportion of their resources must be expended in making combinations, estimates, and adjustments to effect reasonable comparability of areal data. The following summary of the vicissitudes of a large-scale study of population redistribution recounts what must be a virtually universal experience in studies of areal differentiation (Lee *et al.*, 1957, p. 1),

> . . . we share the frustration of all scholars who must deal with ready-made data, and especially of those dependent upon statistics collected for changing administrative uses. We have had to compromise repeatedly: to accept a total time span that was too short, time intervals that were too long, and spatial units that were both too large and too heterogeneous; to be satisfied with residuals when we wanted data on components; to wrestle with difficulties inherent in shifts in administrative definitions and coverage; and to devise indirect substitutes for direct measures.

The authors of the foregoing quotation greatly simplified their problem in one respect, i.e., by utilizing State data throughout their study, despite the unsatisfactory nature of this areal unit for certain of their purposes. But investigators working with smaller areal units must expect to be harassed with problems arising from the instability of areal units. For example, since the establishment of the system of State Economic Areas by the Bureau of the Census in 1951, no less than five different sets of county groupings, all identified as "State Economic Areas," have been employed in the presentation of statistical series by federal and other agencies. Although it is possible in some cases to reconcile these alternative delimitations by recombining county figures, in other cases the requisite raw data are not available. Moreover, the reconstruction of data in this fashion is time consuming and expensive; it makes up an almost prohibitive "overhead" cost for all but the most ambitious studies. This is no isolated example, as can be attested by any research worker who has had to cope with the co-ordination of changing and varying definitions of "industrial areas," "labor market areas," "Standard Metropolitan Areas," and the like.

For reasons that are fairly obvious, it is a general rule that the areal detail of a body of data is likely to be directly related to the degree of aggregation of the data. For example, the figures on industrial classification of the labor force in the 1950 Census of Population are available for small urban places by a 13-category classification; for counties and larger urban places by a 41-item "condensed" classification; and for metropolitan areas, States and larger areas by a 148-item classification; but where industry is cross-tabulated with other variables for the latter areal units, a 77-item classification is used. The design of almost every study of areal differentiation must strike a compromise between the need for areal detail and the need for disaggregated data. It should be understood that this is not merely a technical problem in a narrow sense. It is technically possible with modern tabulating equipment to produce small-area data in as highly disaggregated form as large-area data. However, at a certain point of areal breakdown the data cease to be meaningful. For example, the ultimate breakdown of industry data would yield figures on employment in each establishment. But even if such a breakdown were available on whatever areal basis, the investigator would soon find himself grouping establishments into categories in order to compare areal units. The viewpoint of areal differentiation itself seems, therefore, to imply at least a moderate level of aggregation in areal data. Where a problem is such as to require a maximum of disaggregation, it is likely to be one in which the areal point of view is insufficient in and of itself, though it may provide background for other kinds of research at the "micro" level. The point at which an investigation should switch from or to an areal viewpoint, in terms of its overall objectives, is one that needs careful consideration in each individual case. This appears to be a problem that is seldom adequately discussed.

# CHAPTER 3

# ANALYSIS OF
# AREAL DATA

THE VIEWPOINT adopted in this chapter is that of the investigator manipulating areal data in order to learn something about the universe of territory which he is studying. As has been seen, a typical procedure is to break up this universe of territory into areal units and to compile data for each of these units. The discussion here deals with the treatment of such data after they have been compiled.

We have suggested that the manipulation of areal data may have various objectives. The subsequent discussion is limited to a consideration of four general objectives; these may be listed briefly. The first is simply the *aggregation of areal data* to obtain a datum for the universe of territory. For example, a census office may count the population in each enumeration district, and then add up the enumeration district totals to get the number of inhabitants in the entire territory. Although this example is analytically trivial, there are some more interesting problems connected with aggregation of areal data. In particular, the investigator may have at hand population data which have been aggregated by areal units and face the problem of inferring unknown relationships at the level of the individual from relationships manifest over areal units. (See section 3.1.) A second objective in manipulating areal data is the description or *measurement of areal distributions*. Here the investigator is thinking of the universe of territory as comprising a set of locations distributed over the territory, and areal units are employed as a device for depicting and analyzing such distributions. (See section 3.2.) Thirdly, an investigator may employ areal data to aid in the *analysis of spatial structure,* conceptualized as a pattern of territorial organization. (See section 3.3.) Finally, areal data may be manipulated in the course of an attempt to formulate an *explanation of areal variation* in demographic, social, and economic phenomena. This ordinarily involves description of the ways in which and degrees to which such phenomena vary among areal units, together with the application of some model which is supposed to account for such inter-unit differences. (See section 3.4.) This last type of problem has two special aspects which are considered separately: the problem of *contiguity and regional classification* of areal units (section 3.5), and that of the *temporal aspects of areal variation* (section 3.6).

A common pattern of analysis, for the most part, underlies all these objectives. Information in relatively "raw" form is available for a set of areal units. This information is "processed" by applying various statistical methods to generate a set of data characterizing the several areal units. These are then combined or manipulated in some fashion to yield the desired information on distribution, spatial structure, or areal variation in the universe of territory. It is rarely the case that a simple aggregation, like summing the populations of enumeration districts, is the sole purpose of a study. In general, therefore, we must think of the analysis of areal data as an intermediate step between the collection of information and the statement of inferences about the universe of territory. The main problems considered in the succeeding sections are to characterize the manipulations suggested by the above listed objectives and to consider how the form of the areal data affects the kinds of generalizations about the universe of territory that can be reached.

## 3.1. Aggregation of Areal Data

The relationship between information on the universe and corresponding information on its component areal units is considered here. We are concerned with the logical or mathematical relationships that hold between the two forms of data, not with the problem of estimating universe characteristics from a sample of areal units—a quite different though not wholly unrelated problem. Several cases may be distinguished.

(a) If the areal data are given in the form of frequencies or amounts (e.g., number of inhabitants or acres of land in farms) for the areal units, the corresponding universe datum is the simple summation of the areal data. This holds, of course, for multivariate as well as univariate frequency distributions.

(b) If the areal data are expressed as means, proportions, simple ratios, or rates, the corresponding universe datum is obtained as a *weighted* mean of the areal data. Let $Y_{ij}$ be an observation on the $i^{th}$ individual in the $j^{th}$ areal unit, where $i = 1 \ldots n_j$ and $j = 1 \ldots k$. Then $\bar{Y}_j = \sum_i Y_{ij}/n_j$ is the mean for the $j^{th}$ areal unit, and $\bar{Y} = \sum_j \sum_i Y_{ij}/N$ is the mean for the universe $(N = \sum_j n_j)$. It is easy to see that

$$\bar{Y} = \frac{\sum_j n_j \bar{Y}_j}{\sum_j n_j} = \frac{\sum_j n_j \bar{Y}_j}{N}.$$

One significant application of this point of view concerns the description of change in a universe mean (proportion, ratio, rate). Let the foregoing symbols refer to observations at the initial date of a period, and the same symbols with a prime attached thereto refer to observations at the terminal date. The change in the universe mean then may be expressed as follows:

$$\bar{Y}' - \bar{Y} = \sum_j \bar{Y}_j \left( \frac{n'_j}{N'} - \frac{n_j}{N} \right) + \sum_j \left( \frac{n_j}{N} \right) (\bar{Y}'_j - \bar{Y}_j)$$

$$+ \sum_j (\bar{Y}'_j - \bar{Y}_j) \left( \frac{n'_j}{N'} - \frac{n_j}{N} \right).$$

Now let $p_j = n_j/N$ and $p'_j = n'_j/N'$ be used to represent the proportional areal distribution of the population at the two dates. Using the symbol $\Delta$ for increments, the preceding identity can be written:

$$\Delta \bar{Y} = \sum_j \bar{Y}_j (\Delta p_j) + \sum_j p_j (\Delta \bar{Y}_j) + \sum_j (\Delta \bar{Y}_j) (\Delta p_j),$$

or verbally:

| Change in universe mean | = | (1) Change in areal distribution | + | (2) Change in areal unit means | + | (3) Interaction of changes. |
|---|---|---|---|---|---|---|

In other words, the change in universe mean is broken down into (i) a component of changes in areal distribution (with the initial-date areal unit means as weights), (ii) a component of changes in areal unit means (with initial-date areal distribution as weights), and (iii) an interaction component, which is positive or negative according to whether the changes in areal unit means are positively or negatively correlated with changes in the relative shares of the population allocated to the areal units. (For a more complete discussion, see Kitagawa, 1955; this source indicates alternative ways of expressing a difference between two universe rates in terms of its components; see also Duncan, 1948.)

There are several important implications of the foregoing

relationship. For example, if the interaction term is zero (i.e., the changes in distribution and in areal unit means are uncorrelated), it is possible to have $\Delta \bar{Y} = 0$ despite pronounced changes in areal unit means and in areal distribution. Or, if there are no changes in areal unit means, $\Delta \bar{Y} \gtreqless 0$ according to whether $\bar{Y}_j$ and $\Delta p_j$ are positively correlated, uncorrelated, or negatively correlated. Among other things, therefore, one must recognize the possibility that an apparent equilibrium at the universe level may mask major interacting changes and shifts among the areal units comprising the universe. Moreover, it is possible for change to occur at the universe level with no change in areal unit means, provided only that there is a net shift in population distribution. The substantive importance of this last observation has been indicated by Hoover (1957, p. 66) as follows,

> . . . in per capita measures of economic improvement, it is not correct to consider the national gain or loss as just an average of the regional gains or losses. For example, there can be a rise in national per capita income and welfare, even if every region shows constant or declining per capita income and welfare, provided there is a shift of population from the poorer to the richer regions. Since migration tends to go in that direction, looking at the regional improvement trends alone is likely to give a down-biased view—the national improvement trend may be greater than any one of them.

(c) Various kinds of statistics that can be derived from areal unit data are not readily aggregated to secure the corresponding universe datum. For example, the universe median of a variable, $Y$, is not, in general, a simple or weighted average of the medians of the several areal units. The same is true of other quantiles, the mode, the variance, and the like, as well as indexes (such as the net reproduction rate, for example) computed from formulas involving several operations. In the latter case, one can think of the universe net reproduction rate as an "average" or "weighted average" of the net reproduction rates of the several areal units, but the actual form of this "average" would be quite complicated.

A particular example with considerable didactic value concerns the linear regression and correlation statistics summarizing a bivariate frequency distribution. (The following exposition is based, in part, on W. S. Robinson, 1950.) Let $(X_{ij}, Y_{ij})$ be a bivariate observation on the $i^{\text{th}}$ individual in the $j^{\text{th}}$ areal unit, where $i = 1 \ldots n_j$, $j = 1 \ldots k$, and $\sum_j n_j = N$. By definition, $X_j = \sum_i X_{ij}/n_j$ and $\bar{X} = \sum_j \sum_i X_{ij}/N$, with similar definitions for $Y$.

The "total sum of squares" of $X$ is

$$C_{xxT} = \sum_j \sum_i (X_{ij} - \bar{X})^2.$$

The "within-area sum of squares" is

$$C_{xxw} = \sum_j \sum_i (X_{ij} - \bar{X}_j)^2.$$

The "between-area sum of squares" is

$$C_{xxb} = \sum_j n_j (\bar{X}_j - \bar{X})^2.$$

We have $C_{xxT} = C_{xxw} + C_{xxb}$, with a similar relationship holding for $Y$. The "total sum of products,"

$$C_{xyT} = \sum_j \sum_i (X_{ij} - \bar{X})(Y_{ij} - \bar{Y}),$$

can likewise be expressed as the sum of the "within-area sum of products," $C_{xyw} = \sum_j \sum_i (X_{ij} - \bar{X}_j)(Y_{ij} - \bar{Y}_j)$, and the "between-area sum of products," $C_{xyb} = \sum_j n_j (\bar{X}_j - \bar{X})(\bar{Y}_j - \bar{Y})$.

In terms of the foregoing quantities we may define the "total correlation,"

$$r_T = \frac{C_{xyT}}{\sqrt{C_{xxT} C_{yyT}}};$$

the "average within-area correlation,"

$$r_w = \frac{C_{xyw}}{\sqrt{C_{xxw}C_{yyw}}};$$

and the "between-area" or so-called "ecological" correlation,

$$r_b = \frac{C_{xyb}}{\sqrt{C_{xxb}C_{yyb}}}.$$

Analogously we have the "total regression" coefficient,

$$b_T = \frac{C_{xyT}}{C_{xxT}};$$

the "average within-area regression" coefficient,

$$b_w = \frac{C_{xyw}}{C_{xxw}};$$

and the "between-area regression" coefficient,

$$b_b = \frac{C_{xyb}}{C_{xxb}}.$$

The correlation ratios of the two variables on area are given by

$$E_{YA}^2 = C_{yyb}/C_{yyT} = 1 - C_{yyw}/C_{yyT}$$

$$\text{and } E_{XA}^2 = C_{xxb}/C_{xxT} = 1 - C_{xxw}/C_{xxT}.$$

From these definitions it follows that

$$r_T = r_w \sqrt{1 - E_{YA}^2} \sqrt{1 - E_{XA}^2} + r_b E_{YA} E_{XA}.$$

Express the right-hand side of this equation in terms of the definitions and our proof is concluded as follows,

$$\frac{C_{xyw}}{\sqrt{C_{xxw}C_{yyw}}} \sqrt{\frac{C_{xxw}}{C_{xxT}}} \sqrt{\frac{C_{yyw}}{C_{yyT}}} +$$

$$+ \frac{C_{xyb}}{\sqrt{C_{xxb}C_{yyb}}} \sqrt{\frac{C_{xxb}}{C_{xxT}}} \sqrt{\frac{C_{yyb}}{C_{yyT}}}$$

$$= \frac{C_{xyw}+C_{xyb}}{\sqrt{C_{xxT}C_{yyT}}} = r_T.$$

Similarly, it can be shown that $b_T = b_w + E_{XA}^2 (b_b - b_w)$. Consequently, to express the regression of $Y$ on $X$, $\hat{Y}_{ij} = \overline{Y} +$

$b_T(X_{ij} - \overline{X})$, in terms of the within- and between-area coefficients, we must write

$$\hat{Y}_{ij} = \overline{Y} + [b_w(1 - E_{XA}^2) + b_b E_{XA}^2](X_{ij} - \overline{X}).$$

Two important observations can now be made from the "aggregation" standpoint. First, the "within-area" coefficients, $r_w$ and $b_w$, are not simple or weighted means of the individual within-area coefficients, the $r_j$'s and the $b_j$'s. Instead, $r_w$ and $b_w$ are computed from sums of squares and products pooled over all areal units *before* performing the multiplication, square root extraction, and division involved in the formulas for $r$ and $b$. (This point is perhaps not made sufficiently clear in the cited paper of W. S. Robinson, 1950.) Second, it is not possible to express the universe correlation or regression coefficient ($r_T$ or $b_T$) solely as a function of the corresponding parameters for the areal units. Instead, the universe parameter depends also on the "between-area" relationship and on the "segregation" or degree of areal variation of the two variables, $Y$ and $X$ (as measured by the squared correlation ratios, $E_{YA}^2$ and $E_{XA}^2$). (For a similar theorem relating to regressions based on time series, see Theil, 1954, Chapter II.)

d) The very notion of "aggregation" is applied only equivocally to certain of the kinds of areal unit data described in section 2.2. Suppose, for example, that each areal unit has been classified in terms of the size of the largest urban place contained therein. The size of the largest city in the universe of territory is, of course, in no sense an aggregate or average of the size classifications for the several areal units. One might propose to aggregate the areal data by computing the proportion of areal units with no urban place, the proportion with largest place between 2,500 and 10,000 inhabitants, and so on. But this frequency distribution of areal units is not a universe datum in any unique sense. One cannot infer from it the number of cities in the universe of given sizes, the average size of cities in the universe, or, in fact, any characteristic of the universe that can be specified independently of the particular way in which the universe is broken down into areal units.

Similar examples could be given to show the indeterminate character of the notion of "aggregation" as applied to areal data generated when the areal unit is regarded as a "site or location" (section 2.5), as a "member of a set of areal units" (section 2.6), and "in relation to other units" (section 2.7). This means, in effect, that there are properties both of individual areal units and of aggregates of areal units which lack strict analogues among the properties of a universe of territory. This enhances the impression of the logical complexities involved in manipulations of areal data already gained in the observation that there are properties of areal units, regarded as sub-populations, without analogues among the properties of the individuals making up these populations (see section 2.3). One is led to the platitudinous, but not trivial, comment that an investigator is well advised to have clearly in mind the objectives of his analysis when he ventures to manipulate a set of areal data.

The foregoing discussion indicates severe limitations on the possibility of inferring characteristics of a population or of a universe of territory from characteristics of the areal units into which it has been classified. However, while such inferences may be impossible or unjustified under perfectly general conditions, they may be feasible if some structural limitations are assumed to hold. We shall develop and illustrate one particular possibility of this kind at some length. The discussion will be based largely on two papers by Goodman (1953, 1959) and conversations with him; the numerical examples and their interpretation are ours.

The data concern infant mortality rates for the forty-eight States in 1950. The infant mortality rate is the number of infant deaths, i.e., deaths of persons under one year of age, in a given year divided by the number of live births in that year. We shall be concerned with various classifications of the vital events—color, urban-rural residence, and occurrence of the birth in a hospital vs. occurrence elsewhere.

The total infant mortality rate of an areal unit (the rate for all classes of births), $y$, can always be expressed as a linear combination of its composition and component-specific rates. For example, if we classify births and infant deaths as white or nonwhite, then $y = qx + r(1 - x) = r + (q - r)x$, where $y$ is the infant mortality rate of the area, $x$ is the proportion of births classified as nonwhite, and $q$ and $r$ are the nonwhite and white infant mortality rates of the area, respectively. Now let us suppose that our "aggregation problem" is the following: We know the infant mortality rate, $y$, for each areal unit and the proportion, $x$, of births in each area which are classified as nonwhite. We do not know, however, the component-specific infant mortality rates either for the several areal units or for the population as a whole. It is the latter, $Q$ (nonwhite infant mortality rate in the total population) and $R$ (white infant mortality rate in the total population), which we should like to infer or estimate, making use of our data showing areal variation in total infant mortality rates and proportions nonwhite. Let us consider as a first model which might justify such estimates or inferences the assumption that the component-specific rates, $q$ and $r$, are actually constant from one areal unit to another but that the nonwhite proportion, $x$, varies among units. Then, if one prepares a scatter diagram of $y$ on $x$, it will be found that all the points fall on a straight line,

$y = a + bx$, the intercept and slope of which immediately yield
the component-specific rates, by the formulas $R = a$ and $Q =$
$a + b$. (By assumption, all areal units have the same component-
specific rates; hence $q = Q$ and $r = R$.) In practice, if one had a
set of bivariate observations $(x, y)$ on a set of areal units, he
would not expect all the points to fall exactly on a straight line;
the correlation between $y$ and $x$ probably would be less than
unity in absolute value. However, he might still compute the
least squares regression equation, $\hat{y} = a + bx$, and by analogy
with the foregoing formulas accept as estimates of the component-
specific rates in the total population, $\hat{R} = a$ and $\hat{Q} = a + b$.
This procedure is justified if one can make the assumption, not
that $q$ and $r$ are constant over all areal units, but merely that the
average value of $q$ and the average value of $r$ for all areas with
a given value of $x$ are the same as the average values of $q$ and $r$
for all areas with any other given value of $x$. This might well be
the case even though there was scatter around the regression line
of $y$ on $x$. We shall refer to this method of estimating the presumably unknown component-specific rates of the total population as "Model I." It is characterized by the assumption that the
component-specific rates of the areal units are "practically constant."

Three numerical illustrations using Model I are given, two
of which are "dummy" trials, in that the component-specific
rates of both the areal units and the total population actually are
known, and one of which is more or less realistic and represents
the case in which one might be disposed to use the model to
estimate the unknown component-specific rates of the total population. For the forty-eight States in 1950, the regression of the
infant mortality rate on the proportion of births nonwhite was
computed and found to be $\hat{y} = 27.5 + 20.5x$. The correlation

coefficient corresponding to this regression is .44. The estimated infant mortality rates in the total population yielded by the equation are as follows, shown in comparison with the known actual rates:

|          | Estimated infant mortality rate | Actual infant mortality rate |
|----------|---------------------------------|------------------------------|
| White    | 27.5                            | 26.8                         |
| Nonwhite | 48.0                            | 44.7                         |
| Total    | 30.3                            | 29.2                         |

In this case the model yields quite reasonable estimates, although one would have known that they were somewhat in error by the fact that the estimated infant mortality rate for the two color groups combined was somewhat in excess of the known total rate (this rate would be known in a realistic situation). One therefore may check the reasonableness of his estimates by comparing the known $Y$ with the estimate, $\hat{Y} = \hat{R} + (\hat{Q} - \hat{R})X$, based on the known $X$ and the estimated component-specific rates. A close estimate of $Y$ is a necessary condition for the estimates $\hat{R}$ and $\hat{Q}$ to be close to their true values, but it is not a sufficient condition, as the next example will make clear. Ordinarily, one might be a little hesitant about accepting the estimates of the component-specific rates because of the rather low correlation, .44, between $y$ and $x$. However, as this example shows, if the true values of $Q$ and $R$ are actually quite far apart, the estimates thereof may be reasonably close (in terms of relative error) despite the low correlation.

In the second illustration, the regression of the infant mortality rates for the forty-eight States in 1950 on the proportion of births to residents of urban areas was computed, yielding a correlation of $-.37$. The estimated and actual urban-rural component-specific rates for the total population are as follows:

| | Estimated infant mortality rate | Actual infant mortality rate |
|---|---|---|
| Urban | 23.0 | 28.4 |
| Rural | 38.7 | 30.4 |
| Total | 29.2 | 29.2 |

In this case, although the estimates indicate correctly the direction of the mortality differential, they are rather far off. The accidental identity of the estimated and actual total rates might have given one a false feeling of confidence in the accuracy of the estimates, but he would have been correct in proceeding cautiously in view of the low correlation $(-.37)$ and the appearance of the scatter diagram, which does not exactly suggest a linear relationship.

The third example concerns the regression of the infant mortality rate on the proportion of births occurring in hospitals. For the forty-eight States in 1950, the correlation is $-.61$, and the regression equation yields the following estimates of component-specific infant mortality rates:

| | Estimated infant mortality rate | Actual infant mortality rate |
|---|---|---|
| Births in hospitals | 26.6 | ? |
| Births not in hospitals | 54.9 | ? |
| Total | 30.0 | 29.2 |

In this case we do not know the actual component-specific rates and the question is whether to accept these estimates as reasonable approximations thereto. The estimates are not seriously discredited by the small departure of the estimated from the actual total rate, although, as we saw, the similarity of the two may well be fortuitous. At least by comparison with the two preceding examples, the correlation between $y$ and $x$ is moderately high, although inspection of the scatter diagram might make one reluctant to conclude that the relationship is really linear. Intuitively the mortality differential by hospitalization may seem rather high. However, we have some confidence that it is in the right direction on the basis of a finding by the U. S. National Office of Vital Statistics (1954, p. 20); their study of neonatal mortality (deaths in the first month of life) indicated rates of about 19 and 26 per 1,000 respectively, for hospitalized and non-hospitalized births occurring in the first three months of 1950.

Unless other information can be brought to bear on the problem, the evaluation of the result must depend a good deal on the investigator's judgment as to the plausibility of the assumptions underlying the model. If other information is available on characteristics of the births or of the areal units, it is possible to consider alternative models and, in a sense, to check the results obtained with Model I. Another sort of check may be afforded by employing the same model on different sets of areal units. We shall consider the first possibility, and shall indicate some of its possible ramifications.

In the illustrations thus far we have considered only composition components obtained by a dichotomous classification, e.g., births as white or nonwhite, as urban or rural, etc. One might, however, be interested in composition by an attribute with several categories, such as white, Negro, and other births, or urban, rural-nonfarm, and rural-farm births. Or, composition data might be given in the form of a cross-classification, e.g., births by color and residence simultaneously. Our Model II, then, is suggested on analogy with Model I; it assumes that the component-specific rate for each component is "practically constant" from one areal unit to another. For example, if births are simultaneously classified by color and hospitalization, we may symbolize the infant mortality rate for white births occurring in hospitals by $q_1$, and use the symbols $q_2$ for the infant mortality rate of nonwhite births in hospitals, $q_3$ for the rate for non-hospitalized white births, and $q_4$ for the rate for non-hospitalized nonwhite births. The proportions of births in these four categories are $x_1$, $x_2$, $x_3$, and $(1-x_1-x_2-x_3)$, respectively. We have the identity,

$$y = q_1 x_1 + q_2 x_2 + q_3 x_3 + q_4 (1 - x_1 - x_2 - x_3);$$

this may be written as follows:

$$y = q_4 + (q_1 - q_4) x_1 + (q_2 - q_4) x_2 + (q_3 - q_4) x_3,$$

which is of the form,

$$y = a + b_1 x_1 + b_2 x_2 + b_3 x_3.$$

The multiple regression of $y$ on $x_1$, $x_2$, and $x_3$ may be calculated, and the resulting constants, $a$ and the $b$'s, may be used to estimate the four component-specific $Q$'s in the total population. Presumably the investigator would turn to this model if he judged his assumption that the component-specific rates are "practically constant" to be more credible with a four-component breakdown than with a dichotomous classification. Inasmuch as both color and hospitalization appear to be related to the risk of mortality, this might be an attractive assumption in such an example as ours.

Applying Model II to the 1950 State infant mortality data, one finds a multiple correlation of .69 between $y$ and the combination of $x$'s. The estimated mortality rates from the regression equation are as follows:

|  | Estimated infant mortality rate | Actual infant mortality rate |
|---|---|---|
| White, in hospital | 23.9 | ? |
| Nonwhite, in hospital | 57.7 | ? |
| White, not in hospital | 77.6 | ? |
| Nonwhite, not in hospital | 32.5 | ? |
| All in hospital | 26.9 | ? |
| All not in hospital | 55.9 | ? |
| All white | 27.8 | 26.8 |
| All nonwhite | 46.9 | 44.7 |
| Total births | 30.4 | 29.2 |

Again, one cannot reject the estimates as unreasonable on the basis of the estimated total rate; moreover, the rates for all white and all nonwhite births, derived by weighting the hospital and non-hospital components of each proportionally to their frequency among white and nonwhite births respectively, are fairly accurate estimates of the known white and nonwhite rates. The multiple correlation of .69 is appreciably higher than the zero-order correlation for either color or hospitalization. At first glance it is surprising that among nonwhites the estimated infant mortality rate is lower for non-hospitalized than for hospitalized births, contrary to the situation among whites. It is entirely possible, however, that the kind of selectivity involved in use of hospitals for nonwhite births is different from that operating for white births, i.e., it may be that nonwhites are unlikely to go to hospitals unless there are indications that the birth will involve medical complications. We will not discuss the plausibility of the results further, since the purpose of the illustration is not to reach a substantive conclusion but only to illustrate methodological possibilities. In an actual study, of course, one would wish to consider the probable bias in the rates due to differential under-registration of births, and possibly introduce also the adjustment of the infant mortality rate devised by vital statisticians to take account of annual changes in numbers of births.

A third type of model is generated by introducing an "exogenous" variable. Model III assumes that the *differences* among the component-specific rates, rather than the rates themselves, are "practically constant" from area to area, and that one of the component-specific rates depends on an exogenous variable, $z$. We may state these assumptions in the following form:

(1) $q_1 - q_4 = k_1$

(2) $q_2 - q_4 = k_2$

(3) $q_3 - q_4 = k_3$

(4) $q_4 = a + bz$

(5) $y = q_4 + (q_1 - q_4)x_1 + (q_2 - q_4)x_2 + (q_3 - q_4)x_3$

where we are dealing with a four-category component classification and where the last expression is the identity introduced in connection with Model II. The $k$'s in the first three equations are constants. The fourth equation indicates the assumption that one of the component-specific rates is a linear function of the exogenous variable. By direct substitution we find that the last equation may be written

$$y = a + k_1 x_1 + k_2 x_2 + k_3 x_3 + bz,$$

and we proceed to compute the multiple regression of $y$ on the combination of the three $x$'s and $z$. In the following illustration, our components are again color by place of occurrence (hospital versus non-hospital), and the exogenous variable is median family income in 1949. The multiple correlation is .70, indicating that income adds little to the ability of the composition components to estimate infant mortality. The estimates of component-specific mortality rates obtained from the regression equation are as follows: $\hat{q}_1 = 17.2 + .206z$; $\hat{q}_2 = 49.6 + .206z$; $\hat{q}_3 = 77.5 + .206z$; and $\hat{q}_4 = 34.7 + .206z$; where $z$ is expressed in hundreds of dollars. Since the States varied in median income between about \$1,200 and \$3,700, this means that the estimated infant mortality rate for white births in hospitals varied from about 20 to 25, from the lowest to the highest income State; the estimated rate for nonwhite births in hospitals varied from about 52 to 57; that for non-hospitalized white births varied from 80 to 85; and that for non-hospitalized nonwhite births from 37 to 42. That these rates vary directly with income may seem surprising. However, it must be noted that income is correlated with hospitalization, and one might suspect that in States with high proportions hospitalized, larger proportions of substandard mortality risks tend to be hospitalized. The results for nonwhites again can be rationalized only by supposing a different type of selectivity from that operating for whites. The fact that the coefficient of $z$ is the same for all four component-specific rates is without substantive implications: it is built into the model.

Model IV is somewhat more flexible. In using it, one assumes that each component-specific rate is a separate function of the exogenous variable. For simplicity, we return to the case of a dichotomous classification, for which we may state the assumptions as follows:

(1) $q = a + bx$

(2) $r = c + dx$

(3) $y = r + (q - r)x,$

the last expression being the identity used before. Subtracting equation (2) from equation (1), we have $q - r = (a - c) + (b - d)z$, and hence $y = c + (a - c)x + dz + (b - d)xz$, a linear expression in $x$, $z$, and the product $xz$, whose constants are estimated from the data by multiple regression.

Obviously, more complicated models can be constructed. Additional exogenous variables may be introduced. The relation between one or more of the component-specific rates and the exogenous variable may be assumed to take some form other than linear, for instance a second degree polynomial, and so on. Insofar as finer classifications of components or cross-classifications of two or more components are available, these may be introduced readily. The same sorts of assumptions and procedures are called for in these more complicated models as in those already introduced.

We must leave unexplored the intriguing hunch that models incorporating knowledge of "contiguity" (see section 3.5) could be used to good effect. One might, for example, let the mean of $y$ for adjacent areal units serve as an exogenous variable in Model III or Model IV. Or it might turn out that some other exogenous variable which removed the contiguity in $y$ should be the kind sought for inclusion in these models. That it would be important to take account of "contiguity" seems to follow almost immediately from the discussion of the "modifiable unit" in section 3.4. Here it is shown that, for example, county and State data are not likely to yield the same slope of $y$ on $x$ because of the "contiguity" of counties. If they differed greatly, however, no more than one of these slopes could be a good estimator in our models.

One additional family of models is described in order to bring out an important limitation on the possibilities of inference in this sort of problem. Suppose one took seriously the argument that the selectivity of hospitalized births varied with the extent of hospitalization and consequently wished to consider a model in which the infant mortality rate of hospitalized births is a function of the proportion of births hospitalized. Model V illustrates the possibility of this kind of model; its assumptions are as follows:

(1) $q = k$

(2) $r = a + bx$

(3) $y = r + (q - r)x,$

where $k$ is a constant. This leads to an expression in which $y$ is a function of a second degree polynomial in $x$, i.e., $y = a + (b + k - a)x - bx^2$. If the constants of this equation are obtained by multiple regression, it is easy to ascertain the values of $a$, $b$, and $k$ and use them to estimate $q$ and $r$. But we can also suggest Model V′ with the following assumptions:

(1) $q = c + dx$

(2) $r = k'$

(3) $y = r + (q - r)x$,

where $k'$ is a constant. This set of equations leads to the function, $y = k' + (c - k')x + dx^2$, likewise a second degree polynomial in $x$. As a consequence, if one computes the regression of $y$ on $x$ in the form of a second degree polynomial, he cannot use the results of the computation to ascertain whether Model V or Model V′ is a more appropriate representation of the situation. It might be supposed that one would be better off in postulating that both $q$ and $r$ are, say, linear or parabolic functions of $x$; however, if this assumption is made, the model does not yield the estimates desired. This may be seen by a consideration of Model V″, with the following assumptions:

(1) $q = a + bx$

(2) $r = c + dx$

(3) $y = r + (q - r)x$,

from which it follows that $y = c + (a + d - c)x + (b - d)x^2$. The constant terms in the polynomial can be obtained by multiple regression, but it is impossible to determine the separate values of $a$, $b$, and $d$. It is interesting to note that Model V″ leads to a regression of $y$ on $x$ that is of the same form as that eventuating from Models V and V′.

Three significant observations follow from this example and the preceding discussion. First, in manipulating rate and composition data by regression methods, the regression equations obtained may have quite different interpretations according to the unobservable relationships assumed to underlie them. Second, some of these interpretations can be used to generate estimates of unknown component-specific rates, but others, perhaps equally plausible (such as that of Model V″), do not permit such estimates. Third, the choice among alternative interpretations can never be made solely on the basis of the observed data; it also rests on assumptions made by the investigator and justified to the best of his ability by analogy or partial information.

In the foregoing discussion of models we have indicated that the precise assumptions involved are that the component rates are constant or that they are certain functions of composition or of one or more exogenous variables. In recognition of the fact that these assumptions are unlikely ever to obtain exactly, we have relaxed them by using such terminology as "practically constant" component-specific rates. But once we have gone so far as to acknowledge that the "constant rates" are only "practically constant" and that the postulated relationships are actually equations containing an error term, the use of the intercept and coefficients in the least squares regressions to estimate the component-specific rates may no longer be rigorously justified. The justification for the standard regression approach, therefore, must be pragmatic; that is, that it has the virtue of simplicity and that standard regression methods often are used effectively in situations where they lack rigorous justification, just as statistical inference based on assumptions of normality often is employed when there are known to be departures from normality. Here, as in so many other applications of statistical analysis, the investigator is not relieved of exercising good judgment by the availability of powerful tools for manipulating data.

## 3.2. Measurement of Areal Distributions

Our discussion of this topic will not be exhaustive inasmuch as a fairly thorough survey of the more commonly used techniques of studying population distribution was published recently (Duncan, 1957a,b). Many of these techniques are readily adapted to the measurement of distributions of "populations" other than people. Here we shall indicate some sources where the principal existing techniques are described and then turn our attention to two specific approaches in order to bring out several salient problems.

Without attempting a refined or exhaustive classification, we may identify four major approaches or groups of techniques developed for the study of areal distributions. (a) First, a considerable variety of *cartographic techniques* have been developed to depict distributions and to portray variations in density and similar ratios. A recent summary of literature on population geography (James, 1954) provides a good orientation in these techniques. (b) Recently, social scientists and geographers have become interested in the tests for randomness of distributions devised by phytosociologists and plant ecologists. Since few distributions of human population are random, however, there is even greater interest in the several proposals for measuring the patterns of distribution. Pertinent surveys of literature are available in Curtis and McIntosh (1950), Goodall (1952), and Clark and Evans (1954). The last reference, in particular, develops the idea of characterizing a distribution in terms of mean distance of each member of the population to its nearest neighbor. The technique would appear promising as a means of investigating the spacing of cities and settlements (Duncan, 1957a, pp. 32-34). It is being applied in this and other ways by geographers, particularly a group working at the University of Washington (Seattle); thus far, however, their research has appeared mainly in a series of preliminary "discussion papers," which are described as "not ready for critical comment and appraisal in publications."

(c) A third approach involves use of centrographic techniques—stemming from various approaches to the calculation of a "center" of population, which have undergone considerable elaboration. These are described, for example, by Sviatlovsky and Eells (1937) and Hart (1954). Much of the pertinent literature is in Italian and has not been widely read in English-speaking countries. A contribution by Bachi (1958) is discussed subsequently. The calculation of population potential, described in section 2.7, can perhaps be regarded as a variant of centrographic techniques, although it was developed independently thereof (see Duncan, 1957a, p. 37). (d) Finally, mention is made of the several types of coefficients and indexes of areal distribution developed from or closely related to Lorenz-curve analysis of distributions (Wright, 1937; Hauser, Duncan, and Duncan, 1956; Thompson, 1953). These include the indexes variously labeled as measures of geographic association (Florence, *et al.*, 1943), segregation (Duncan and Duncan, 1955b), and localization. Some discussion of this class of indexes follows.

An important way in which techniques of measuring distributions can be characterized—to signalize an unresolved problem —is the classification of techniques into a) those whose results are intrinsically dependent on the way in which the universe of territory is subdivided into areal units and b) those whose results depend only incidentally on the system of areal units. A subclassification of the latter might distinguish between measurements (for example, certain centrographic ones) that are dependent on the directions in which co-ordinate axes run and those that are invariant under rotation of axes.

The following paragraphs set forth an illustration of the application of the "index of concentration" to certain areal distributions. The problem of interpreting the results for alternative sets of areal units is emphasized. The data pertain to the census years, 1900 to 1950. The following systems of areal units are considered: (a) counties, which number about 3,000 though they vary in number from census to census; (b) State Economic Areas, which number 443 and are combinations of counties (the SEA system employed here distinguishes metropolitan from non-metropolitan areas); (c) economic subregions, which number 119 and are combinations of SEA's (economic subregions may include SEA's lying in different States, and most metropolitan SEA's do not constitute separate subregions); (d) the forty-eight States and the District of Columbia; and (e) the 9 geographic divisions delimited by the Bureau of the Census, which are combinations of States.

The index of concentration represents a specific application of the more general index of dissimilarity to the measurement of population concentration; its use for this purpose has been set forth by Hoover (1941, 1951). The index of population concentration, where $x_i$ is the per cent of the United States population residing in the $i^{th}$ areal unit and $y_i$ is the per cent of the land area of the United States contained in the $i^{th}$ unit, can be expressed as

$$\Delta = \frac{1}{2} \sum_{i=1}^{k} \left| x_i - y_i \right|,$$

where $k$ areal units make up the United States. (In using this formula, one usually computes the sum of the positive and negative differences, $x_i - y_i$, separately. A quick computational check is available, for the two sums must be equal.) Alternatively, one may identify all areal units with population densities greater than the density for the United States as a whole. The index of concentration can be expressed as the difference between the percentage of the United States population residing in the "above-average density" areas and the percentage of the United States land area contained in the same set of areas. The index of concentration, then, is a simple measure of displacement. It can be interpreted as the percentage of the national population which would have to move from their area of present residence in order to make the densities of all areal units equal (disregarding any unevenness *within* areal units).

From its definition it is apparent that the index of concentration will vary according to the system of areal units for which it is calculated. In general, the smaller the average size of areal unit, the larger the index value. More precisely, if one system of areal units is derived by subdivision of the units of another system, the index computed for the former can be no smaller than the index for the latter, and usually will be larger. Thus the index of concentration on a county basis will exceed the index on a State basis, because the county index takes into account intrastate concentration.

The upper panel of Table 2 shows indexes of concentration for five sets of areal units, 1900 to 1950. The same data are shown graphically in Figure II. In each year the value of the index increases as the areal subdivision becomes finer. But the significant result of these calculations is that the several time series of indexes do not move together. This finding has several important implications:

(a) On the basis of the index of concentration, or any similar measure, one cannot assign a unique meaning to the notion of "degree of population concentration." Such an index has meaning only in terms of the specific set of areal units for which it is computed.

(b) Divergent changes in the several series indicate that the pattern of population redistribution is complex. The following hypotheses are consistent with the observations, but are not necessarily demonstrated by them: (i) The decrease in concentra-

## Table 2
### Indexes of Population Concentration and Net Population Redistribution, for Various Systems of Areal Subdivision of the United States: 1900 to 1950

| Year or period | Areal Units* | | | | |
|---|---|---|---|---|---|
| | Geographic Divisions | States | Economic Subregions | State Economic Areas | Counties |
| **Indexes of Concentration:** | | | | | |
| 1950 | 39.2 | 42.2 | 50.1 | 55.8 | 58.9 |
| 1940 | 40.5 | 42.2 | 49.2 | 53.7 | 59.1 |
| 1930 | 40.8 | 42.8 | 49.1 | 53.4 | 55.9 |
| 1920 | 41.2 | 43.9 | 48.3 | 51.8 | 53.8 |
| 1910 | 41.6 | 44.9 | 48.7 | 51.3 | 52.8 |
| 1900 | 43.6 | 48.0 | 51.6 | 53.3 | ... † |
| **Indexes of Net Redistribution:** | | | | | |
| 1940-50 | 3.0 | 3.8 | 4.5 | 5.6 | ... † |
| 1930-40 | 1.6 | 2.0 | 2.2 | 2.9 | ... |
| 1920-30 | 2.2 | 3.6 | 4.9 | 6.2 | ... |
| 1910-20 | 1.7 | 2.4 | 4.2 | 5.5 | ... |
| 1900-10 | 3.7 | 4.1 | 6.0 | 7.3 | ... |

* For all units except counties, boundary changes were disregarded. 1950 land area figures were used for Geographic Divisions and States, and 1940 figures for Economic Subregions and State Economic Areas. For counties the census area figures for the specified year were used.
† Not computed.

tion shown for "large" units like States and divisions may reflect a gross smoothing out of population distribution over the continental area, a continuation of the east-west pattern of settlement. (ii) The decrease in concentration for the decade 1900-10 shown by indexes based on subregions, SEA's, and counties (although the 1900 county index was not computed, it must have been higher in 1900 than in 1910 to be consistent with the 1900 index based on SEA's) probably means that this gross redistribution overshadowed any local patterns of redistribution that would

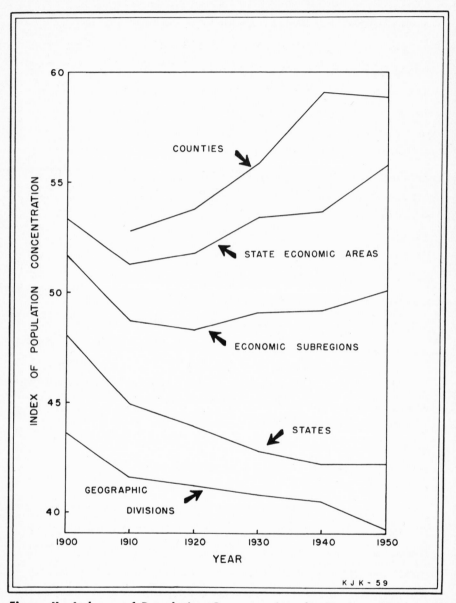

**Figure II. Indexes of Population Concentration, for Various Systems of Areal Subdivision of the United States: 1900 to 1950.**

also be reflected in the indexes. (iii) The increases in the county indexes, 1910-40, the SEA indexes, 1910-50, and the subregion indexes, 1920-50, doubtlessly represent urban and metropolitan concentration occurring concomitantly with the broad regional deconcentration evidenced in the State and division indexes. (iv) The slight decrease in the county index, 1940-50, probably represents deconcentration within metropolitan areas occurring concomitantly with the disproportionate growth of entire metropolitan units, as reflected in the increase, 1940-50, in the index based on SEA's. (v) Irrespective of the detailed validity of these interpretations, the observed changes in index values must be explained empirically, for they do not merely reflect formal properties of the index numbers. No single series is adequate, by itself, to bring out the pattern of changes in population distribution that occurred during the first half of the century. Still other patterns of redistribution probably would be revealed by indexes based on other types of areal units.

(c) Indexes computed for SEA's behave somewhat like indexes based on counties, possibly because both reflect the process of metropolitan concentration. SEA's exhibit this pattern probably because they were delimited so as to isolate the metropolitan units, as of the end of the period under examination. On the average, metropolitan areas manifested disproportionate growth during the period 1900 to 1950. Had the SEA's been delimited prior to 1900, with their boundaries remaining fixed thereafter, much urban-metropolitan concentration could have occurred *within* SEA's; in this case, it would not have been reflected in the series of concentration indexes. Indexes based on SEA's might then have shown relatively slight increases in concentration since 1910, as was true of the indexes based on subregions.

Another type of index can be computed conveniently (except for counties, for which indexes of concentration were computed by the alternative method previously described) with the data assembled to compute indexes of concentration. This is the "index of net redistribution" of population, values of which are shown in the lower panel of Table 2 and in Figure III. The formula is the same as that given for the index of concentration, except that $y_i$ is now the per cent of the population residing in the $i^{th}$ areal unit in a given year and $x_i$ is the per cent residing there in an earlier year. The index, interpreted as a measure of displacement, shows the minimum percentage of persons who would have had to change their areas of residence in a given year to produce the per cent distribution of an earlier year. The index does not measure solely the magnitude of migration between the two dates, even in net terms, since changes in distribution can be produced by areal differences in natality or mortality as well. However, migration is, no doubt, the major component in population redistribution. As in the case of the index of concentration, the absolute size of the index of net redistribution varies inversely with the size of areal unit or fineness of the system of areal subdivision.

Synchronous fluctuations in the four series of indexes are observed. Although the rates of change differ among the four series, the indexes move up and down together. The differences in rates of change of the indexes do not suggest any readily summarized pattern. The parallel fluctuations probably represent decade-to-decade variations in rates of population mobility. Some basis for this interpretation is found in the following tabulation, which compares the index of net redistribution on a State basis (from Table 2) with changes in the per cent of the native population residing in States different from the State of birth:

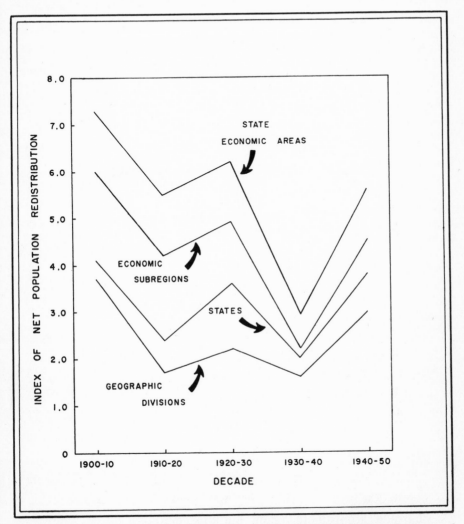

Figure III. Indexes of Net Population Redistribution, for Various Systems of Areal Subdivision of the United States, by Decades: 1900 to 1950.

| Decade | Index of net redistribution | Change in per cent in different State |
|--------|-----------------------------|--------------------------------------|
| 1940-50 | 3.8 | 3.2 |
| 1930-40 | 2.0 | − 1.0 |
| 1920-30 | 3.6 | 1.3 |
| 1910-20 | 2.4 | 0.5 |
| 1900-10 | 4.1 | 1.0 |

These two series tend to move together; this suggests that temporal variations in the index of net redistribution reflect the general level of population mobility rather than the specific pattern of redistribution.

Results like the foregoing would be regarded as evidence of the inappropriateness of the measure of areal distribution used, if one accepted the following criterion set forth by Bachi (1957, p. 3),

> As we are . . . interested in studying the general characteristics of the geographical distribution, we may want to calculate summary indices for this distribution, which should be independent of the manner of division into districts usually used.

The indexes of distribution suggested by Bachi are based on the centrographic approach. Some elements of this approach are well known, but it seems worthwhile to summarize certain of its extensions.

Suppose the location of the $i^{th}$ areal unit in the territory whose population distribution is to be measured is given by a horizontal co-ordinate, $X_i$, and a vertical co-ordinate, $Y_i$, and let its population be $f_i$. (Bachi sometimes speaks of a "longitude" and "latitude" co-ordinate system, but appears to base his calculations on a square-grid system.) Then the "mean center" of the population (what the United States Bureau of the Census calls the "center of population") is located at $(\bar{X}, \bar{Y})$, where $\bar{X} = \sum_i f_i X_i / \sum_i f_i$, and $\bar{Y} = \sum_i f_i Y_i / \sum_i f_i$. Bachi proposes (apparently independent of the same proposal by Furfey, 1927) as a measure of dispersion around the mean center the "standard distance,"

$$d = \sqrt{\frac{\sum_i f_i (X_i - \bar{X})^2}{n} + \frac{\sum_i f_i (Y_i - \bar{Y})^2}{n}},$$

where the summations are over all $k$ areal units and $n = \sum_i f_i$.

There is an interesting theorem relating the standard distance to the mean quadratic distance among the individuals in the population, computed on the assumption that each individual is located at the center of his areal unit. Let $d_{ij}$ be the distance between the centers of areal units $i$ and $j$, given by

$$d_{ij} = \sqrt{(X_i - X_j)^2 + (Y_i - Y_j)^2}.$$

The mean quadratic distance is defined by

$$D = \sqrt{\frac{\sum_i \sum_j f_i f_j d_{ij}^2}{n^2}}.$$

It can then be shown that $D = d\sqrt{2}$ (cf. Yule and Kendall, 1950, p. 147). Thus the dispersion of the population around its mean center turns out to bear a constant relationship to its dispersion as measured by distances separating individuals in the population. The values of $d$ and $D$, then, are invariant under rotation of the $X$ and $Y$ axes and their calculation depends only incidentally on the subdivision of the territory into areal units. Their values, in general, are somewhat more precise if there are many small areal units than if there are only a few large ones.

Bachi suggests various norms for use in interpreting the magnitude of $d$, including hypothetical values of $d$ computed on the assumption of even distribution of population (i.e., all areal units having the same density) or on the assumption that the $f_i$ are assigned at random to the areal units. We shall not reproduce the pertinent formulas here, but shall indicate one other important application of the underlying ideas.

Suppose the population is classified into two or more categories on the basis of some qualitative or quantitative characteristic. The mean center is calculated for each category separately as well as for all categories combined. Compute (a) the pooled sum of squares of distances of all individuals in the several categories to the centers of the respective categories, and (b) the weighted sum of squares of the category centers to the general center, with the respective category populations as weights. Then $e = \dfrac{(b)}{(a) + (b)}$ is a measure of the proportion of the total sum of squares of distances from the general center "explained" by the classification of the population into categories. It is thus analogous to the squared correlation ratio ($E^2$, as defined in section 3.1) of a variable on an attribute.

Bachi suggests the following method of cartographic representation of the standard distance. From the origin at $(\bar{X}, \bar{Y})$ draw four line segments of length $d$ with end points at $\bar{X} \pm \sqrt{\sum_i f_i (X_i - \bar{X})^2 / n}$, $\bar{Y} \pm \sqrt{\sum_i f_i (Y_i - \bar{Y})^2 / n}$. This figure not only represents the dispersion in terms of the standard distance but also its "latitude and longitude components." Bachi fails to point out, however, that although $d$ is invariant under rotation of reference axes, the values of its two components change with such rotation. Hence the suggested graphic representation cannot be said to depict the areal distribution in a unique manner. Furfey (1927) considers still another type of figure related to the mean center and standard distance which may be used as "a graphic representation of the form of the distribution, or as an indication of the amount of scatter," but concludes that it is inadequate for either purpose.

Comparison of the materials on the index of concentration with the extensions of centrographic methods developed by Bachi brings out clearly the difference between measures of areal distribution that depend intrinsically on the system of areal subdivision and those that depend only incidentally on the areal units. There is much to be said for Bachi's criterion, which gives a clear preference to the latter. However, the fact that indexes of concentration and like measures are dependent on the system of areal units does not imply that they are empirically meaningless, even though the investigator is at liberty to work with alternative sets of areal units. As we attempted to bring out in comparing results based on alternative sets of areal units, the time series for each set appears to yield information not fully conveyed by any other set. Moreover, it seems likely that any single centrographic measure would be insufficient to bring out the several aspects of change in a pattern of distribution. One may suppose, therefore, that further development of centrographic techniques—or other methods with similar desirable properties—is necessary before the dispensing with all measures not meeting Bachi's criterion can be justified.

As Wright (1937, esp. pp. 178 and 205) indicated, one encounters unanticipated complexities in trying to devise measures of the unevenness of areal distributions that are independent of the method of areal subdivision. Although the matter requires further study, one might conjecture that any such measure must, implicitly or explicitly, turn on the measurement of distances. The centrographic techniques and the measures of spacing developed in plant ecology (Clark and Evans, 1954) illustrate the explicit use of distance. The "index of centralization" (described by Hauser, Duncan, and Duncan, 1956, pp. 42-49) is an example of an index into which distance measurement enters implicitly, and whose value is independent, except for errors of approximation, of the method of areal subdivision.

## 3.3. Analysis of Spatial Structure

Our discussion of this large topic will be brief. Seemingly there is little that can be said on the subject in general terms that has concrete methodological value. The kinds of researches that appropriately are classified under this heading are highly diverse, and most of them are tentative explorations of a problem whose contours are just beginning to be glimpsed. The techniques thus far used or proposed are rather intimately related to the conceptual frameworks employed by the respective investigators, and the methodological transfer value of such techniques for alternative frameworks is often difficult to establish. Moreover, a number of proposals remain unimplemented for lack of data.

Before offering a couple of general observations, we may point out some of the kinds of contribution being made to the development of techniques for analyzing spatial structure.

(a) Although they are not usually categorized as such, some of the more theoretically oriented approaches to the study of migration patterns certainly qualify as contributions to the analysis of spatial structure. One contribution is the "model of intervening opportunities" elaborated by Stouffer (1940). This model asserts that the volume of out-migration from an areal unit to destinations at various distances from it is directly proportional to the number of "opportunities" for migrants in a distance band and inversely proportional to the number of "opportunities" at all lesser distances. Such a model may be used to calculate the expected proportions of migrants travelling various distances, and this frequency distribution, or relevant parameters thereof, may then be said to describe the spatial structure of migratory flows over the territory. (See Isbell, 1944; T. R. Anderson, 1955; and literature there cited.) Several other kinds of migration models are described by Hannerberg *et al.* (1957). We might also mention the somewhat related fields of "diffusion models" as represented, for example, by the work of Hägerstrand (1952), and "linear programming transportation models" as represented, for example, by a paper of Garrison and Marble (1958).

(b) Another important group of studies deals with the spatial structure of the division of labor. These have taken various forms; e.g., the empirical delineation of market and supply areas; the construction of more or less hypothetical schemes of relationships among areal units based on the central-place concept; and investigation of gradient and other patterns of areal differentiation in economic activity viewed as indicators of complementary specialization. An instance of the latter approach is Bogue's (1949) investigation of the structure of the metropolitan community conceptualized in terms of relationships between dominant metropolitan centers and tributary portions of the metropolitan region. Isard and Whitney (1949) analyze data in a somewhat similar fashion to infer a division of labor between central and outlying portions of the metropolitan region in respect to various types of retail outlets. Direct techniques for delimiting urban "fields" and "umlands" on the basis of traffic flow data and the like are discussed by Godlund (1956).

(c) A number of suggestive ideas and promising leads for research have been set forth by Vining (1949, 1953, 1955). His developments are based on the premise that "we should explicitly introduce a spatial dimension into our conception of the economic structure of the nation" (Vining, 1949, p. 90). He (1953, p. 52) has utilized data on commodity flows, population distribution, and cyclical fluctuations in economic activity in various ways to bring out the implications of the viewpoint that,

> the economy, in its spatial aspects of structure and functioning, is to be regarded as a continuum. It occupies area but it is not to be identified with the area occupied, and it has an objective form of its own as *pattern* and *structure*. The economy is an organization of economizing units. The behavior to be studied is not that of the units but rather of the system of units. . . . A statistical description of the form and pattern assumed by this system may be made . . . without reference to any particular set of geographic sub-areas.

A somewhat related approach is that of Hanna (1957b), who proposes regression methods for studying the dependence of the economic growth of the component areal units on the growth of the national economy.

(d) Among the more elaborate techniques for investigating the interrelationships of areal units composing a national economy is the "interregional input-output model" proposed by Isard (1951). Aside from the difficulties encountered in implementing this model with the requisite data, the whole approach appears to raise certain unresolved questions about the delimitation of appropriate sets of areal units. For example, Isard (1951, p. 320) states: "It is desirable to mark off regions which exhibit self-sufficiency with respect to a maximum number of like goods and services." Such a criterion would appear to beg the question, unless "self-sufficiency" can be measured independently of the flows between regions and industries which the input-output model is designed to represent. In all fairness, however, it should be pointed out that similar issues yet to be satisfactorily resolved are raised by the other approaches to analysis of spatial structure mentioned here.

(e) As a final item in an incomplete list, we mention the so-called "gravity models," which represent, in part, applications and elaborations of the "population potential" concept outlined in section 2.7. Harris (1954), for example, has advanced the understanding of the localization of manufacturing by treating the concentration of manufacturing in the northeastern manufacturing belt not merely as a problem in distribution but as a problem of bringing theoretically relevant data to bear on the identification of forces producing the spatial pattern of industry. An excellent review of studies using "gravity models" is provided by Carrothers (1956); see also Stewart and Warntz (1958).

The main point we wish to emphasize is the interrelationship between the analysis of spatial structure and other approaches to the study of areal differentiation. The former is characterized by a more sophisticated conception of its purposes; it seems to favor the development of somewhat complex models and analytical tools; and it clearly seeks to go beyond the merely descriptive presentation of areal data that is typical of much work on areal distributions and areal variation. Thus the distinction among approaches pertains more strictly to the purpose and method of analysis than to the kinds of data analyzed. Students of spatial structure often resort to a study of areal distributions in an effort to infer patterns of relationship among areal units. A recent contribution on "Population Distribution and Community Structure" (Duncan, 1957b) raises anew the perennial issue of the validity of such inferences.

Another point of contact between analysis of spatial structure and other interests in areal differentiation is the use of structural concepts and hypotheses to explain or predict patterns of distribution or of areal variation. A large volume of research on urban areal differentiation, for example, has proceeded without the benefits that can be derived from this type of theorizing. Hawley and Duncan (1957) have called attention to the need for theories of spatial structure as a basis for such research.

A comparison of alternative views of the problem of spatial structure raises in perhaps its clearest form the issue stated in section 1.2—that of the attitude taken toward areal units. As has been seen, Vining has suggested a viewpoint on the analysis of spatial structure which requires that such structure be described "without reference to any particular set of geographic sub-areas." By contrast, in discussing uses of the interregional input-output model, Isard appears to suggest that there is a theoretically optimum system of areal units; and elsewhere he raises the possibility of a unique set of optimum if not ontologically "real" areal units called "regions" (Isard, 1956). Now this issue—which we might label the "nominalist" versus the "realist" concept of areal units—has been so thoroughly discussed (see, e.g., Hatt, 1946; James and Jones, 1954, Chapter II) that the marginal return on further debate must be zero, if not negative. (Similar issues arise in other fields of inquiry. For example, sociologists have a running battle on whether "social classes" are merely analytical constructs of the student of social stratification, or "real" units of social organization.) There is one consideration, however, that we should like to point out. Many researchers on areal differentiation are forced to work with prefabricated areal units which they accept for reasons of convenience and expediency; moreover, as we have indicated, the results of manipulating areal data often are to some degree dependent on the choice of a set of areal units. Consequently, present practice in research can be fully satisfactory neither from the extreme "nominalist" viewpoint (because the description can only be given in terms of a particular set of areal units) nor from the extreme "realist" viewpoint (since prefabricated areal units are not "real" regions). How this problem may be resolved cannot be foreseen. But it appears that men trying to develop cogent theories of areal structure will have to reckon with it for some time to come. Meanwhile, students of areal structure must take into account the discrepancy between their hypothetical constructs and their actual results which is generated by the necessity of working with systems of areal units for which data are available.

## 3.4. Explanation of Areal Variation

> It does not matter where the cycle of observation-hypothesis-theory-verification begins. It may be at times useful to begin with theory *in abstracto* and at other times with the compilation of data. The cycle must be traversed several times anyway before a coherent picture can arise. One suspects that questions of scientific strategy have no general answers. Different situations and, significantly, different scientific temperaments call for different approaches.
>
> —ANATOL RAPOPORT

The study of areal differentiation as the geographer has traditionally conceived it has been distinguished from the interest in areal variation on the part of sociologists, demographers, human ecologists, and economists. In brief, the chorographic approach leads to a concern with describing and interpreting differences *among areas* and with ascertaining what makes one area different from another. The other kind of interest involves analysis of areal variation in a *class of phenomena*—economic, demographic, or social—defined from the standpoint of a particular conceptual scheme or frame of reference. That there is this real and important difference between the emphases of "chorographic" and "systematic" research does not gainsay the fact that the two are oftentimes closely related in terms of sources of data, techniques of analysis, and so on. Indeed, the difference may lie more in the ultimate objectives of an analysis than in the kind of analytic procedures employed. Be that as it may, we are here concerned with the problem of areal variation as social scientists have generally attacked it, rather than with the chorographic problem as such.

The typical history of a study in areal variation may be outlined hypothetically as follows: An investigator, having chosen a subject for study in terms of its relevance to some conceptual framework—let us use the example of mortality analysis in demography—observes that differences among areas represent an aspect of the variation in those indicators or measurements he proposes to study. For example, he observes that States, counties, or cities differ in respect to their death rates. Such an observation immediately poses a problem. On the one hand, he knows that any explanation of variation in death rates that he may formulate will be incomplete unless it explains or accounts for these areal variations. On the other hand, he may suppose that the areal variation of mortality, or the pattern which such variation takes, may suggest the nature of the variables responsible for mortality variation in general. At this point, various alternatives are open to him. He may decide to neglect the analysis of areal data for the time being, and concentrate on such factors as age, sex, social status, or heredity, assuming that once he has identified the major causes of mortality variation he will simultaneously have discovered the reasons for the variation among areal units. The test of this assumption, although it comes at the end of the investigation, should not be omitted, inasmuch as there is always the possibility that some factor or class of factors which is necessary to account for areal variation remains unidentified. The likelihood that this will be true seems high, for at least some causally relevant factors in mortality appear to be area-specific, e.g., traffic density, climatic conditions, and environmental hazards. The other alternative is to set up the study initially to deal with areal variation, using areal data as one of the major resources of the research. In such a case the investigator will select characteristics of areal units which he believes to have a bearing on their differential mortality, incorporating these in some kind of explanatory model whose adequacy he can test by seeing whether it accounts for areal differences. Factors whose importance is established by the analysis of areal data, however, cannot be presumed sufficient to explain other types of differential mortality. For example, it would have to be shown that the variables accounting for inter-area differences in death rates explain occupational differences in mortality *within* areal units. Indeed, we may have to contemplate the possibility that an explanatory model is necessarily relative to the areal framework within which the dependent and the explanatory factors are assumed to operate. As the analysis moves from the individual level to one which deals with aggregate statistics for large populations of individuals, one thing which can occur is the disappearance of the influence of factors that might have had considerable explanatory value at the individual level. For example, let us assume that smoking habits are significantly associated with risk of mortality at the individual level. To use this same variable at the areal level will not be fruitful if the *average* patterns of smoking habits of areally classified populations do not differ greatly. At the areal level, then, it would not be surprising to find that no significant correlation exists while at the individual level a significant correlation obtains. It can happen, then, that as one moves up the "aggregation ladder" certain influences may be cancelled out. In any case, whether or not the investigator initially lays emphasis on areal variation, his study of such a phenomenon as mortality is incomplete unless at some point this source of variation is explicitly taken into account.

At some stage of any investigation which is concerned explicitly with areal variation it is likely to be noticed that such variation is not spatially random, but rather that areal units in the same vicinity tend to resemble each other, for instance, in respect to their death rates. How the investigator should cope with or capitalize on this circumstance is a moot question, some aspects of which are set forth in section 3.5. At this point it may merely be noted that some research workers are inclined to exploit the notion of "homogeneous regions," attributing to it a certain explanatory value, whereas others take the position that regional variation is merely a species or pattern of areal variation which, though it may complicate the analysis of the latter, is to be explained on the same generic grounds. In either case, although there are various ways of proceeding, the investigation can no more justify logically neglecting regional variation than it could justify ignoring areal variation itself.

An additional contingency to be reckoned with in the kind of study we are outlining is that phenomena subject to areal variation often are subject as well to temporal variation. It sometimes happens that explanatory models which are very successful in accounting for cross-sectional or "static" differences, areal or otherwise, may not afford even a partial explanation of temporal changes. Moreover, the pattern of areal variation may undergo change—some areas, for example, may lower their death rates sooner or more rapidly than others. This phenomenon cannot be neglected in an inquiry whose objective is to understand how things work in the real world. Again, however, there are difficult and disputed questions as to the way in which studies of temporal variation should be co-ordinated with analyses of areal variation; some of these issues are set forth in section 3.6.

In summary, our viewpoint in this section is that of the research worker searching for an acceptable "explanation" of the observed areal variation of a phenomenon which is interesting to him. It is possible to set forth some considerations as to various contingencies that may be encountered in such a search without attempting to resolve all the issues suggested by the various connotations of the concept of "explanation" or by a philosophic consideration of the role of "explanation" in science. However, we do wish to clarify our point of view in certain particular respects.

In the first place, one must acknowledge the fact that the investigation of areal variation (particularly with respect to economic quantities) often is carried out in the context of the discussion of social policies. For this reason, it is important to remember that *evaluation is not explanation.* As Vining (1953, p. 51) states,

> . . . judgments . . . are daily made to the effect that per capita incomes in certain areas are *too low* or that industrial development of certain areas is *lagging* or that the structures of the economies of certain areas are *out of balance.* But upon inquiry into the bases of these judgments, one must agree, I believe, that they issue from our passions and sympathies, and one will search in vain for analytical criteria that will stand critical investigation. There are analytical criteria in economic theory by which the consistency of an argument in a social discussion may be judged. But no positive theory now exists which will account for the structural and operating features and developmental processes of a human economy as it performs under acceptable conditions of freedom for individual units and which would assist participants in a social discussion in evaluating how well or how poorly an existing economy is performing and in making explicit the

meaning of some such notion as "significant divergence" from "proper performance."

In other words, a meaningful appraisal or evaluation of areal variation presupposes some acceptable explanation thereof. The analyst who begins with normative considerations uppermost in his mind may well be deflected from a path which·would lead to a satisfactory explanation which might even be of use in implementing his norms.

Another type of discourse, although it may be relevant to or of heuristic value in explaining areal variation, is not to be confused therewith. We refer to what economists call "theory" or "economic analysis." For our purposes, what distinguishes conclusions reached in economic analysis from those acceptable as explanations of areal variation is the abstractness of the former. The economist may reason, for example, that in a competitive economy with perfect mobility of the factors of production there would be no areal variation of average income. If, then, areal variation of income is observed, it must be "explained" by constraints on the operation of competition or frictions working to retard mobility. (The argument is simplified in order to bring out the main point quickly.) If the argument were begun, as is usually the case, by stipulating that "other factors" are outside its scope, then the "explanation" comes down to a tautology, assuming that the various steps in the argument are logically correct. As Holt (1954, p. 434) cautions, we must continually guard against the

> confusion between formal validity and material truth. Logical consistency within a set of axioms is sufficient to ensure formal validity, but material truth requires a correspondence between an hypothesis and phenomena in the real world. How much nonsense has been written because a formal theorem in geometry or calculus has been confused with an empirical statement about the world?

The trouble with the "explanations" provided by economic analysis for such phenomena as areal variation in income, is that they work equally well for all instances of such variation. To convert the "theoretical explanation" into the type of "explanation" we have in mind, it would be necessary to show that in a concrete instance, where valid indicators of the degree of imperfection in competition and of the rate of mobility are at hand, knowledge of such indicators would enable one to estimate with reasonable accuracy the relative income levels of the areal units making up a population of such units. In other words, from the point of view taken here, an "explanation" does not consist merely in suggesting the factors involved in, or even the general form of a relationship; it must also include an estimate of the actual parameters of an empirical relationship and a demonstration that these parameters satisfactorily account for the variation in a body of actual data. The requirement of specificity, if it may be so called, does not, of course, foreclose the possibility that an investigator seeking an "explanation" of areal variation will find valuable suggestions in the various bodies of theory and their explanatory principles.

The concrete view of the problem of explaining areal variation which we are taking here implies that a necessary—though, quite possibly, not sufficient—condition for accepting an explanation is that it provides a model with acceptable "goodness of fit" to a concrete set of observations on a specified universe of areal units. Without prescribing the form which such a model must take or the manner in which it is derived, we may note that establishing "goodness of fit" usually comes down to something like determining the regression of a dependent variable on one or more explanatory variables. Regression methods are, in fact, finding a great deal of favor among students of areal differentiation, including those approaching the problem from a geographic point of view (e.g., McCarty *et al.,* 1956; Robinson and Bryson, 1957), as well as from an economic (e.g., Ruttan, 1955) and demographic (e.g., Bogue and Harris, 1954) viewpoint. Most such investigators are aware of many unresolved problems surrounding the application of regression techniques to areal data, and we shall not restate those problems that have received adequate attention in the cited literature. In fact—without prejudice to other approaches—we shall assume that the case for regression techniques in the analysis of areal variation has been adequately stated and that the essentials of these techniques are already known or are readily accessible to the reader (see, particularly, Bogue and Harris, 1954).

We may distinguish three broad and overlapping categories of uses of regression techniques. The first is the calculation of correlations more or less blindly as a means of generating hypotheses. For example, Sanderson (1954, pp. 61-62) refers to the practices of certain

> "crop forecasters" who embark on their analyses with little knowledge of the underlying relationships and who start out by plotting as many monthly means of temperature, rainfall, sunshine or humidity as are available against final yield. Those meteorological series which show an apparent correlation with yield are then used to construct a forecasting formula. In other words, the procedure consists in selecting, out of a larger number ($N$) of series originally considered, that set of ($M$) variables which yields the highest multiple correlation coefficient, corrected for degrees of freedom. The only restriction imposed on the choice of variables is the requirement of general "plausibility."

While there is no fundamental logical objection to this method of hypothesis formulation, if no superior alternative is available, it must be clearly understood that the data used to construct an hypothesis in this fashion cannot then be used to test it. The test must be a completely independent procedure, based on independent data.

The second use of regression techniques, then, is to test hypotheses carefully specified in advance. We do not review the nature and underlying assumptions of statistical tests, on which topics the reader may consult standard statistical texts or, e.g., Sanderson (1954, Chapter III). However, it is appropriate to comment on what is and what is not established by such tests, having in mind their substantive interpretation rather than the probability statements to which they lead. It would appear that this interpretation depends somewhat on the status of the hypothesis. If this hypothesis has been derived in the manner described above, the test merely serves to verify the stability of the correlation pattern previously observed and to establish whether or not it may be considered reliable for forecasting or estimating purposes under conditions comparable to those of the test. A purely empirical result, though confirmed in independent experience, has limitations from a scientific standpoint, whatever its pragmatic uses may be. For one thing, the judgment that "comparable conditions" obtain when it is applied in new situations is one that must be made on extraneous grounds; it really implies that the research worker has knowledge going beyond that incorporated in his regression model. For this reason, there is a certain futility about the conventional hortatory statement about replication—e.g., Bogue and Harris (1954, p. 3): "explanations must be taken as tentative and preliminary until supported by research which covers additional periods of time." The interpretation is somewhat different if the hypothesis under test is one that has been rigorously derived from a theory for whose postulates there is some degree of independent support. In this case, failure of the hypothesis to withstand examination leads to rejection or reformulation of the theory. If the hypothesis is sustained, the theory cannot be said to be "verified," but it can at least be considered to be strengthened. At the same time, acceptability of the hypothesis itself does not rest on the statistical test alone, since it bears a relationship to other hypotheses which have been supported by evidence. The theoretical structure then provides grounds for deciding whether the "comparable conditions" obtain for the use of the regression relationship in explanation, estimation, or forecasting. The role of the theoretical framework is nicely brought out in Simon's (1957, Chapter 2) discussion of the problem of "spurious correlation." We should also like to call attention to the enlightening paper by Wold (1956), which discusses the important issue of whether and how "causal inferences" may be justified when the investigator has at his command only "observational" rather than "experimental" data. This, of course, is the typical predicament of the student of areal variation. It might be helpful in future discussions of this problem— which has much too wide ramifications to follow out here—to make a distinction between "causal relevance" and "causal specificity." In presenting (sections 3.1 and 3.5) examples of correlations of infant mortality with income we are aware that dollars do not kill babies or prevent their death. We would depend on medical personnel to identify the "cause of death," and if we were searching for immediate circumstances attending the incidence of such causes, we should probably not begin our search with incomes. At the same time, we have reason to believe that areal differences in income are connected ("causally," if you will) with differences in housing standards, diets, medical care, etc., which, in turn, are connected with conditions affecting the probability of incidence of a cause of death. Without elaborating the argument, it can be seen that the "causal relevance" of income might well be established, though no high degree of "causal specificity" could be attributed to this factor, as far as mortality is concerned.

The third use of regression arises when the investigator possesses, or is possessed by, a theory which gives him a relatively complete account of the structural relations holding in the situation under study and his application of regression or related techniques is designed only to estimate the parameters of these structural relations. Here it is assumed that the process by which the data were generated is known; hence the empirical analysis is designed to reflect the essentials of that process. It is mainly the specialists in econometrics (cf. Beach, 1957, Chapter 10) who have developed regression techniques from this viewpoint. As yet, the econometric approach has been applied relatively little to conventional sorts of problems in analysis of areal variation, and we shall not need to comment further on it except to remark that the relatively sophisticated integration of theory and research which it embodies may be kept in view as a model for less developed fields.

In the remainder of this section we wish to discuss only two technical problems of regression analysis that are somewhat peculiar to its application in the analysis of areal data. Both problems have been discussed in the literature; but both merit greater attention than they have received as well as additional methodological study.

The first problem arises from the fact that areal units are what Yule and Kendall (1950, Chapter 13) term "modifiable units." For example, in working out a problem in the areal variation of a demographic phenomenon, the investigator may have a choice as to working with counties, State Economic Areas, or States, each larger unit of which series comprises a combination of the smaller units. Now, it is easy to show that correlation and regression results obtained from one such set of areal units will, in general, differ from those obtained from another set. We return to the equations introduced in section 3.1, giving them a slightly different interpretation:

$$r_T = r_w \sqrt{1 - E_{YA}^2} \sqrt{1 - E_{XA}^2} + r_b E_{YA} E_{XA},$$

and

$$b_T = b_w + E_{XA}^2 (b_b - b_w).$$

Here we are thinking of $(X_{ij}, Y_{ij})$ as a bivariate observation on the $i^{th}$ unit of a set of "small" areal units (e.g., counties) located in the $j^{th}$ unit of a set of "large" areal units (e.g., States). Hence the "total correlation," $r_T$, and the "total regression," $b_T$, are those obtained from county data, and the "between-areas" correlation and regression, $r_b$ and $b_b$, respectively, are those obtained from State data, if the State data are taken as unweighted means of the counties contained in the several States, and if these data are weighted by the number of counties per State in computing the correlation and regression on a State basis. Ordinarily, we compute from State data without taking account of the county data, and under these conditions the relations between State and county results are somewhat indeterminate, inasmuch as States differ in the number of counties they contain, and counties vary in size. It would be only an accident, however, if these differences should operate in such a way as to make the correlations and regressions from State and county data identical.

Yule and Kendall give a model of an "attenuation effect," which they suggest may sometimes account for the differing results secured from different orders of areal unit. We believe that this phenomenon is more probably related to the existence of "contiguity," as that concept will be developed in section 3.5. To give the concept a concrete interpretation, counties in the same State resemble each other more closely than would counties selected at random from all States; thus the correlation ratios in the foregoing equations usually differ significantly from zero.

There are, of course, problems in which one type of areal unit is more or less "natural"; for example, a study of per capita expenditures for highways would probably be carried out on a State basis, because highway funds are collected and disbursed by States, or are allocated to States by the federal government. However, in a study of levels of living or of mortality there may be no compelling reason a priori to regard State data as more or less meaningful than county data. In such a case the investigator may be well advised to work with alternative sets of areal units and perhaps actually to calculate values to substitute in the equations given above, in order to understand something of the implications of the choice of areal unit for the interpretation of his results. Unfortunately, we are unable to offer more specific guidance on this problem. It may be that there is no general resolution of it, and that each investigation must develop its own qualifications and interpretations with the aid of whatever substantive considerations may come to mind. After some extensive consideration of the problem of "scale," McCarty *et al.* (1956, p. 16) conclude,

> In geographic investigation it is apparent that conclusions derived from studies made at one scale should not be expected to apply to problems whose data are expressed at other scales. Every change in scale will bring about the statement of a new problem, and there is no basis for presuming that associations existing at one scale will also exist at another.

The second kind of problem pertains to the case in which the areal data are in the form of averages, rates, proportions, and the like, derived from distributions of attributes and variables in the respective populations of the areal units; i.e., the areal unit is regarded as a collection of items. The question here is whether relationships between characteristics of the items established for the population as a whole may be of use in explaining variation in characteristics of areal units—in one sense, the inverse of the "aggregation problem" treated in section 3.1. If, for example, it is known that in the United States the infant mortality rate is higher for nonwhites than in the white population, one might seek an explanation of State differences in infant mortality in terms of the variation by States in proportion of nonwhites. It is important to note, however, that one cannot immediately general-ize from the "individual correlation" between color and mortality to the conclusion that color composition explains areal varia-tion in mortality rates, or even that any large proportion of the inter-area variation in mortality is accounted for by variation in color composition. This is brought out clearly in the following rearrangement of the equation set forth in section 3.1:

$$r_b = \frac{r_T - r_w \sqrt{1 - E_{YA}^2} \sqrt{1 - E_{XA}^2}}{E_{YA} E_{XA}}.$$

Here $r_b$ is the correlation computed from the areal data, $r_T$ is the correlation from the individual data for the whole universe of territory, $r_w$ is the average within-area individual correlation, and the correlation ratios indicate the extent of areal differentia-tion of the two characteristics. It is clear that $r_b$ cannot be in-ferred from a knowledge of $r_T$ alone without the information on areal differentiation of the characteristics. Moreover, even the sign of $r_b$ is not necessarily the same as that of $r_T$.

An illustration of a case where a known individual correla-tion is of no help in explaining areal variation concerns sex differences in infant mortality. In the United States in 1950, the infant mortality rate per 1,000 live births was 32.8 for males and 25.5 for females. There is, therefore, an appreciable relationship between sex and risk of mortality on the individual level. However, for this relationship to be of any value in explaining *areal* differences in infant mortality, it would be necessary for areal units to differ appreciably in their sex ratios at birth. Actually they do not, apart from chance variations attributable to small numbers of births. In the United States the proportion of males at birth runs around 51.3 per cent. Variation by States in this proportion seldom falls outside the limits of 50.5 per cent to 52 per cent (Chambliss, 1949). Given the United States infant mortality rates by sex in 1950, one can calculate that the total infant mortality rate would be 29.2 if 50.5 per cent of the births were males and 29.3 if 52 per cent of the births were males. Obviously State differences in infant mortality cannot, to any significant degree, be explained by the sex difference in mortality.

The problem under discussion here is one familiar to demographers under the heading of "population composition" and "compositional components" of rates of various kinds of events. We shall discuss this problem in some detail and with some formality. The justification for emphasizing it is two-fold. First, while demographers have developed various techniques of so-called "standardization" that are applicable to the problem, these seem not to be well known to other research workers. Second, demographers have failed to provide a wholly satisfactory rationale for the selection and application of standardization techniques and, particularly, for the decision to use them in place of alternative techniques. For the most part, they have followed various rules of thumb in calculating standardized rates and have relied on a body of lore concerning their interpretation. While we shall not expound all aspects of standardization, the framework of our discussion should prove helpful in developing a systematic treatment of the subject.

We assume a population classified according to location in one of the $n$ areal units making up the universe of territory and simultaneously according to some characteristic with $m$ categories. The categories, for example, might be class intervals of income, residence categories (e.g., urban, rural nonfarm, and rural farm), sex, or color, and so on. They might well be categories produced by the cross-classification of two or more attributes, such as age-sex categories, or income-color-residence categories. We let the areal units be identified by the index $j = 1, 2, 3, \ldots n$, and the categories of the characteristic by the index $i = 1, 2, 3, \ldots m$. We may then define the population matrix, $\mathbf{P}$, as the array in $m$ rows and $n$ columns of the population frequencies, $P_{ij}$, which stands for the number in the $i^{\text{th}}$ category and the $j^{\text{th}}$ areal unit. Associated with $\mathbf{P}$ are the row of column totals, $P_{.j} = \sum_i P_{ij}$, the column of row totals, $P_{i.} = \sum_j P_{ij}$, and the total population of the universe, $P_{..} = \sum_i \sum_j P_{ij} = \sum_i P_{i.} = \sum_j P_{.j}$.

The composition matrix, $\mathbf{X}$, is obtained from $\mathbf{P}$ by dividing each entry in $\mathbf{P}$ by the total of its column; thus $X_{ij} = P_{ij}/P_{.j}$ is the proportion of the population of the $j^{\text{th}}$ areal unit that falls into the $i^{\text{th}}$ category of the characteristic by which the population is classified. Hence $\sum_i X_{ij} = 1.0$. The composition of the total population is represented by a column whose typical entry is $X_{i.} = P_{i.}/P_{..}$ and whose total, $\sum_i X_{i.}$, likewise equals unity. From the column totals of $\mathbf{P}$ we also derive the proportional distribution of the universe population by areal units, expressed as the proportion $X_{.j} = P_{.j}/P_{..}$ of the total population located in the $j^{\text{th}}$ areal unit; note that $\sum_j X_{.j} = 1.0$.

Associated with each area-category segment of the population, $P_{ij}$, is a corresponding frequency or magnitude of an event, attribute, or variable that characterizes that segment. We shall denote it by $L_{ij}$ and refer to the $m \times n$ matrix **L**, whose typical entry is $L_{ij}$, as the "incidence" matrix, for lack of a better term. $L_{ij}$ might represent, for example, the number of deaths occurring during a certain year in the sub-population $P_{ij}$, the number in that population who are members of the labor force on a given survey date, or the total income received by that population during a specified period. The marginal totals of **L**, $L_{i.} = \sum_{j} L_{ij}$ and $L_{.j} = \sum_{i} L_{ij}$, and the grand total of all its entries, $L_{..} = \sum_{i} L_{i.} = \sum_{j} L_{.j}$, are counterparts of the marginal and grand totals of the entries of **P**.

With the data of **P**, **L**, and associated marginal and grand totals, we may construct the "rate" matrix **Y**, a row of area-specific rates, a column of category-specific rates, and the universe rate. The typical entry in **Y**, $Y_{ij} = L_{ij}/P_{ij}$, is the quotient of the incidence frequency or magnitude divided by the number in the sub-population. In referring to the $Y_{ij}$ as "rates," we are broadening the usage of the term to include not only quantities which conventionally are designated as incidence rates (e.g., death rates) but also proportions, means, and per capita ratios. (This wider usage of the term, which is adopted solely for expository convenience, is also found in Kitagawa, 1955.) We define as area-specific rates $Y_{.j} = L_{.j}/P_{.j}$, as category-specific rates $Y_{i.} = L_{i.}/P_{i.}$, and as the universe rate $Y_{..} = L_{..}/P_{..}$. We may state some elementary but useful theorems concerning rates and composition. First, the universe rate is the weighted average of the area-specific rates with the distribution of the population by areal units as weights:

$$Y_{..} = \sum_j X_{.j} Y_{.j};$$

it is also the weighted average of the category-specific rates with the universe composition as weights:

$$Y_{..} = \sum_i X_{i.} Y_{i.}.$$

Second, the area-specific rate, or the rate for the $j^{th}$ areal unit, is the weighted average of the sub-population rates with the weights given by the composition of the areal unit:

$$Y_{.j} = \sum_i X_{ij} Y_{ij}.$$

Note that in both these statements it is unnecessary to show the sum of the weights in the denominator of the weighted mean, since in each instance that sum is unity. The third theorem, however, requires explicit inclusion of the sum of weights. The attribute-specific rate for the $i^{th}$ category of the universe population is the weighted mean of the sub-population rates with the areal unit composition as weights:

$$Y_{i.} = \frac{\sum_j X_{ij} Y_{ij}}{\sum_j X_{ij}}.$$

Each of the foregoing theorems is easily verified by substituting for the rate and composition terms their definitions in terms of incidence and population and simplifying the resulting expressions.

We may now indicate some alternatives and contingencies with respect to the analysis of a body of data like that just described. This will serve as a prelude to a more extended discussion of a particular kind of problem that is fairly frequently encountered in the analysis of areal variation.

Where the information contained in the rate matrix **Y** is of primary interest and the investigator is concerned with variation of rates by both categories and areal units, recourse may be had to techniques of multivariate analysis. The $m \times n$ array of rates may be analyzed, for example, as a two-way analysis-of-variance problem. (See, e.g., Yule and Kendall, 1950, sections 22.17-22.19.) Another alternative is exemplified by Kendall's (1939) study of crop yields. In his problem acreage corresponds to our "population," per-acre yields to our "rates," and crops to our "categories." Using analysis of principal components, Kendall established an index of general productivity for the counties of England. H. Smith (1954) suggests the same technique for studying areal variation in age-specific death rates. Note that in such examples what we term "composition" does not, or at least need not enter.

A second kind of alternative is the calculation of index numbers for the several areal units to render the area-specific rates comparable with respect to composition. The logic of index numbers has been explored most thoroughly by economists in connection with such problems as that of measuring change in the general level of prices. The formulas for price indexes may be applied here by taking our "rates" as the equivalent of the economist's "prices"; "composition" or "population" as the equivalent of his "quantities"; "categories" as the equivalent of "commodities," and "areal units" as the counterparts of "years." Our "universe" then represents one possibility for a counterpart to the "base year" used as a norm of comparison in the price index number. An index number corresponding in form to the Laspeyres price index can be expressed,

$$\frac{\sum_i X_{i.} Y_{ij}}{\sum_i X_{i.} Y_{i.}} = \frac{\sum_i X_{i.} Y_{ij}}{Y_{..}}.$$

This is also equivalent to the "comparative mortality figure" sometimes computed in connection with "direct standardization" in mortality analysis, where the "rates" are death rates and the "composition" is by age intervals. An index number corresponding in form to the Paasche price index is

$$\frac{\sum\limits_{i} X_{ij} Y_{ij}}{\sum\limits_{i} X_{ij} Y_{i.}} = \frac{Y_{.j}}{\sum\limits_{i} X_{ij} Y_{i.}};$$

this is equivalent to the "standard mortality ratio" sometimes computed in connection with "indirect standardization" in mortality analysis. The reader acquainted with either the literature on index numbers or that on mortality analysis will recognize the possibility of still other types of index numbers. We have some preference for the index number version of standardization procedures over the presentation of so-called standardized rates in the analysis of areal variation in mortality. This preference is based largely on the danger that unsophisticated readers will misinterpret standardized rates. Unless one is experienced in their use, there is a temptation to think of standardized rates as representing something more than results of a hypothetical calculation. The index number form keeps the underlying assumptions in the forefront of attention. We are inclined to think, however, that for many problems in areal variation some of the other techniques mentioned here are likely to be more enlightening than either standardization or calculation of index numbers by the usual formulas.

We next consider the formulation of the problem in terms of composition as an explanatory variable in the analysis of area-specific rates. A highly important contingency here is that not all of the data described earlier will be available to the analyst. In particular, it may happen that the category-specific sub-population rates (the $Y_{ij}$) and the incidence data from which they are computed (the $L_{ij}$) are not available, even though area-specific and category-specific rates (the $Y_{.j}$ and $Y_{i.}$) are available for the universe along with the composition data ($X_{ij}$ and $X_{i.}$) for both the universe and the areal units. There are various reasons why the rates may not be available. For example, owing to legal restrictions, votes for candidates are not tabulated by characteristics of voters, although they are published in summary form for areal units. Oftentimes, in using census statistics, the investigator is interested in rates that could be computed only from cross-tabulations that have not been prepared by the census office. Or suppose the investigator is interested in the difference in infant mortality rates between births occurring in hospitals and those occurring elsewhere because he suspects that a part of the areal variation of infant mortality rates is due to differential accessibility and use of hospital facilities. To compute infant mortality rates specific for hospitalization would require data compiled by matching each infant death certificate with the corresponding birth certificate to determine whether the birth occurred in a hospital. Such matching is expensive, and it is not done as a part of routine vital statistics tabulations. Hence it is ordinarily not possible to compute mortality rates for the hospitalized and non-hospitalized categories.

A frequent situation with published statistics is that rates are available for the universe but not for the areal units, i.e., the $Y_{ij}$ are lacking but the $Y_{i.}$ are available. In the voting statistics example and that of the hospitalized vs. non-hospitalized births, category-specific rates are available neither for the areal units nor for the universe; both the $Y_{ij}$ and the $Y_{i.}$ are lacking. In this connection we may call attention to a similarity of the subject under discussion here to that treated in section 3.1, where we showed that if the $Y_{i.}$ are unknown it may be possible to estimate them from the composition data, $X_{ij}$, and area-specific rates, $Y_{.j}$. This use of regression rests on assumptions about the unknown $Y_{ij}$ and the investigator would, of course, always prefer not to have to make such assumptions. Although the central problem in this case is to estimate the unknown universe category-specific rates, as a step in the procedure one obtains the correlation between area-specific rates and composition of areal units. This correlation, in some sense, is a measure of the degree to which composition explains areal variation in rates. (We shall qualify this statement presently.)

The use of regression to estimate the influence of composition on areal variation in rates need not, of course, be confined to the case in which the $Y_{i.}$ are unknown. One might suppose, in fact, that a common device for studying composition as a factor explaining areal variation in rates would be to compute the multiple regression of the $Y_{.j}$ on the $X_{ij}$. However, we are not familiar with many examples of this procedure. (One would, of course, have to omit one of the $X_{ij}$ from the battery of independent variables, inasmuch as $\sum_i X_{ij} = 1.0$ by definition; to use all $m$ of them would, therefore, involve a system of $m + 1$ equations to be solved for $m$ unknown coefficients.) The procedure which we wish to illustrate, a variation on what demographers know as the "method of expected cases," resembles this regression approach in that the $Y_{.j}$ are related to a linear combination of the $X_{ij}$; but the weights used in making this combination are not those determined on a least squares criterion but are rather a set of arbitrary weights. In the particular version of the method we consider, they are, in fact, the universe category-specific rates, the $Y_{i.}$.

We obtain the "expected rate" for the $j^{\text{th}}$ areal unit by the formula $E_j = \sum_i X_{ij} Y_{i.}$; i.e., the expected rate is a linear combination of the universe category-specific rates, $Y_{i.}$, in which the weights are the composition of the areal unit. (It may be seen that $E_j$ is the denominator of the Paasche-type index number or standard mortality ratio mentioned earlier; calculation of $E_j$ is the first step in so-called indirect standardization.) One can interpret $E_j$ as a measure of the proneness of the composition of the $j^{\text{th}}$ areal unit toward high or low rates. If its composition is such that a disproportionate share of its population is in categories having high universe rates, $E_j$ will be higher than the expected rate for the average areal unit; if its population is concentrated in low-rate categories, its expected rate will be correspondingly low. (We may note here that the weighted mean of the $E_j$, with the distribution of the population by areal units as weights, is equal to the universe rate: $\sum_j X_{.j} E_j = Y_{..}$.)

The comparison between the actual rate for an areal unit, $Y_{.j}$, and the expected rate, $E_j$, indicates whether the actual exceeds or falls below an expectation based on the areal unit's composition and an average set of category-specific rates. There are several ways of making and summarizing this comparison. If the ratio of the actual to the expected rate is considered meaningful, one may compute $Y_{.j}/E_j$, the index number mentioned above. In the usual form of indirect standardization, this ratio is multiplied by $Y_{..}$ (the universe rate). An alternative is to consider the departure from expectation as given by the algebraic difference, $Y_{.j} - E_j$; if a standardized rate is desired, it may be obtained as the expression, $Y_{..} + Y_{.j} - E_j$. A third alternative is to compute the correlation between $Y_{.j}$ and $E_j$ and to regard its magnitude as indicative of the extent to which composition explains areal variation in rates. This seemingly obvious expedient, so far as we know, has not been used by demographers, despite their familiarity with the expected cases technique. There are, however, examples of its use by economists (Perloff, 1958; Hanna, 1957a). It was in the discussion of one of these examples by George H. Borts (1957) that important qualifications on the interpretation of such a correlation came to light. Our presentation of the matter differs somewhat from the published discussion by Borts; it is based in part on suggestions received in personal correspondence with Borts and with Richard F. Muth, neither of whom, of course, is responsible for the use made of his suggestions.

Let us consider a numerical example (taken from Duncan, 1959b). The areal units are the 35 municipal wards of the City of Montreal, Canada. The 1941 Canadian census provides information on the religious classification and the ethnic (so-called "racial origin") composition of the population residing in each ward. Our "rates" are the percentages of the population classified as Catholic in each ward and in the city as a whole. Our "composition" is given by the proportions of each ward population and of the city population in the dozen ethnic categories. The expected rate, therefore, is calculated by applying the city ethnic-category-specific rates of Catholic affiliation to the ethnic composition of the areal unit. Figure IV shows a scatter diagram in which the actual percentages of Catholics by ward are plotted against the expected percentages. The two obviously are closely similar, and the correlation between them is quite high, 0.99. Apparently, ethnic composition in large measure explains the areal variation in percentage of Catholics in Montreal. The question is seen to call for closer analysis, however, when we note that the departure of actual from expected rates is more often positive when the expected rate is high than when it is relatively low, despite some exceptions to this tendency. The

interpretation of this result is aided by referring to the slope of
the regression of actual on expected Catholic percentages; this
slope, approximately 1.09, is significantly higher than unity,
according to a one-tail $t$-test, which yields a probability below
0.005 that the difference is due to chance. (The somewhat skewed
distribution of the percentages may be noted as a qualification

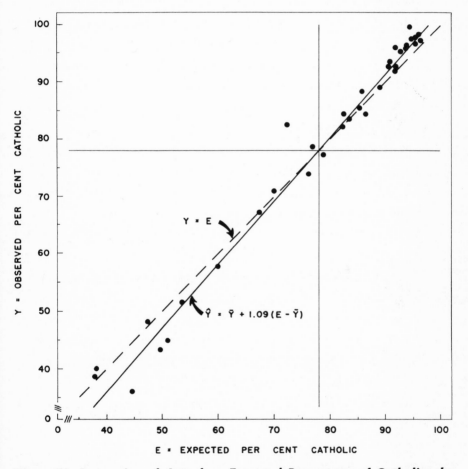

*Figure IV. Regression of Actual on Expected Percentage of Catholics, by
Municipal Wards, City of Montreal, Canada, 1941. (Source: 1941 Census
of Canada.)*

on the applicability of this test.) As is shown by the algebraic relationships presented below, the departure of the slope from unity requires that we attribute less influence to composition as such than we would infer on the basis of the correlation coefficient alone.

It will simplify the following to assume that the actual and expected rates are expressed as deviations from their common (weighted) mean. Lower case letters are used to denote the variables in this deviation form. We omit the subscript identifying the areal unit, since all summations are over $j$. For consistency, we must assume that all means, variances, and coefficients are computed with the $X_{.j}$ as weights. With this understanding, we will not bother to write the weights. Thus, the slope of $y$ on $e$, $b_{ye}$, is expressed as $\Sigma ye/\Sigma e^2$, which is defined to mean $\sum_{j} X_{.j} y_{.j} e_j / \sum_{j} X_{.j} e_j^2$. Whether or not this weighting is of practical consequence in an actual calculation depends on the variability of areal units in respect to population size. We have not bothered with it in the example of Montreal Catholic percentages, which was worked out primarily for illustrative purposes. In section 2.4 reference was made to views of A. H. Robinson (1956) in favor of weighting.

Referring again to Figure IV, we see that, taking the mean as origin, the two lines plotted on the diagram are $y = e$ and the regression $\hat{y} = be$. Let $v$ stand for the departure of an actual rate from the first line, i.e., for the difference $y - e$; and let $u$ be the residual $y - \hat{y} = y - be$ from the regression line. We may then write

$$y = be + u \tag{1a}$$

$$y = e + v. \tag{1b}$$

We propose that the question of whether composition explains areal variation in rates be phrased in terms of how much of the variance of $y$ is accounted for by composition. Let us express the variance of $y$ in the following forms suggested by equations (1):

$$\sigma_y^2 = b^2\sigma_e^2 + \sigma_u^2 \tag{2a}$$

$$\sigma_y^2 = \sigma_e^2 + 2\,\text{cov}\,(ev) + \sigma_v^2. \tag{2b}$$

Equations (2) are obtained by squaring and summing over $j$ (with appropriate weighting, as noted above) equations (1a) and (1b) respectively. It will be noted that equation (2a) has no covariance term, since it is a property of least squares linear regression that $e$ and $u$ are uncorrelated. In (2a) we have the conventional two components of variance, $b^2\sigma_e^2$, the variance "explained" by regression, and $\sigma_u^2 = \sigma_y^2 - b^2\sigma_e^2$, the "unexplained" variance. Equation (2b) gives a rather different decomposition of variance. However, we may put the two versions together by noting the equality of the right-hand term in (2a) to that in (2b), whence it follows that $b^2\sigma_e^2 = \sigma_e^2 + 2\,\text{cov}$ $(ev) + (\sigma_v^2 - \sigma_u^2)$. Here the term in parentheses is necessarily non-negative since the least squares criterion requires $\sigma_u^2 \leqslant \sigma_v^2$. Our decomposition of the variance of the rates, therefore, looks as follows:

| | |
|---|---|
| Total | $\sigma_y^2$ |
| Explained by regression | $b^2\sigma_e^2$ |
|     $A$. | $\sigma_e^2$ |
|     $B$. | $2\,\text{cov}\,(ev)$ |
|     $C$. | $\sigma_v^2 - \sigma_u^2$ |
| Unexplained | $\sigma_u^2 = \sigma_y^2 - b^2\sigma_e^2$ |

Taking note of certain identities will aid in the interpretation of this decomposition. It is obvious at once that components $C +$ "unexplained" $= \sigma_v^2$; hence

$$A + B = \sigma_y^2 - \sigma_v^2.$$

Recalling that $v = y - e$, we see that

$$\sigma_y^2 - \sigma_v^2 = (2b - 1)\sigma_e^2,$$

since

$$\Sigma y^2 - \Sigma(y - e)^2 = 2\Sigma ye - \Sigma e^2 = 2b\Sigma e^2 - \Sigma e^2$$
$$= (2b - 1)\Sigma e^2.$$

With this value of $(A + B)$ and $\sigma_e^2$ for $A$, it follows at once that $B = 2(b - 1)\sigma_e^2$. We may also obtain an alternative expression for component $C$ by noting that $C = \text{``explained''} - (A + B) = b^2\sigma_e^2 - (2b - 1)\sigma_e^2 = (b - 1)^2\sigma_e^2$.

Our interpretation of the several components of variance and combinations thereof is as follows. $(A + B)$ is the "gross effect of composition," for if $\sigma_v^2$ represents the variation around the line $y = e$, then $\sigma_y^2 - \sigma_v^2$ represents variation accounted for by that line. If every actual rate equalled its expected rate, all points would lie on the line with $\sigma_v^2 = 0$, and all the variation in $y$ would be accounted for by composition. Component $C$, then, is a portion of the variation in $y$ explained by regression of $y$ on $e$ but in no sense by composition as such; hence we refer to it as "net effect of (unknown) variables associated with composition." Breaking $(A + B)$ down into its separate components, we identify $A = \sigma_e^2$ as the "net effect of composition" and $B$ as the "joint effect of composition and (unknown) variables associated with composition." This interpretation may be clarified by returning to our original full notation. Note that the observed rate, $Y_{.j}$, may be expressed as $\sum_i X_{ij} Y_{ij}$. Hence the equation $Y_{.j} = E_j + V_j$, may be written

$$\sum_i X_{ij} Y_{ij} = \sum_i X_{ij} Y_{i.} + \sum_i X_{ij}(Y_{ij} - Y_{i.}).$$

The product of the two terms on the right, which is involved in cov $(ev)$, is seen to have one "rate-constant" factor but one term in which there is variation of rates over areal units. We should not wish to attribute variance contributed by the *rate* differences $(Y_{ij} - Y_{i.})$ to composition, although these differences may be correlated with composition. Note that cov $(ev)$ may be positive, zero, or negative according as $b > 1$, $b = 1$, or $b < 1$, since we showed that $2 \text{ cov } (ev) = 2(b-1)\sigma_e^2$. In summary, our decomposition of variance may be tabulated as follows:

| | | |
|---|---|---|
| Total | $\sigma_y^2$ | |
| Explained by regression | $b^2\sigma_e^2$ | |
| A. Net effect of composition | $\sigma_e^2$ | $A + B$ = gross effect of composition |
| B. Joint effect of composition and (unknown) variables associated therewith | $2(b-1)\sigma_e^2$ | $B + C$ = gross effect of variables associated with composition |
| C. Net effect of variables associated with composition | $(b-1)^2\sigma_e^2$ | |
| Unexplained by regression | $\sigma_y^2 - b^2\sigma_e^2$ | $C$ + unexplained = net effect of differences between areal unit rates and universe rates |

The decomposition of variance evidently furnishes an assessment of the extent to which composition explains areal variation in rates which is preferable to that suggested merely by correlating actual and expected rates—the procedure referred to at the outset of this discussion. Incidentally, it can be shown that this correlation, $r_{ye} = \sigma_e/\sigma_y + r_{ev}\sigma_v/\sigma_y$, for if we square this correlation to ascertain the proportion of variance explained, the right side of the equation yields three terms which reduce, respectively, to components $A$, $B$, and $C$, each divided by $\sigma_y^2$.

It may be of interest to summarize the findings on the Montreal religion data. Expressing the components of variance as percentages of total variance, we have the following:

| | |
|---|---|
| Total | 100.0 |
| Explained by regression | 98.0 |
| $A$. Net effect of composition | 82.9 |
| $B$. Joint effect of composition and factors associated therewith | 14.5 |
| $C$. Net effect of factors associated with composition | 0.6 |
| Unexplained by regression | 2.0 |

This example is significant in indicating that one can easily over-estimate the net effect of composition by examining only the correlation between actual and expected rates. Even though this correlation is very high and the slope, $b_{ye}$, departs from unity to what may seem to be only a moderate extent, the interaction component, $B$, is not negligible, and ethnic composition as such by no means explains the Catholic residential distribution completely. (For further substantive interpretation see the cited paper by Duncan, 1959b.)

## 3.5. Contiguity and Regional Classification

Sooner or later in a study of areal variation the investigator runs up against the fact that areal units situated close to each other are more likely to be similar in their characteristics than are areal units which are some distance apart or areal units grouped together at random. The use made of such a finding varies with the purpose of the research. Students with a geographic orientation are inclined to view the similarity of adjacent areal units as a clue to the existence of "regions"; in fact, a considerable literature on delimitation of "homogeneous regions" has developed around the problem of how best to recognize spatial groupings of similar contiguous areal units (see, for example, Kendall, 1939; Hagood et al., 1941; Hagood, 1943; Bogue, 1951, 1955). By contrast, the methodologist interested in criteria for establishing interrelationships among various types of areal variation may regard the similarity of adjacent areal units as something of a nuisance, or at least as a problem that must be solved before the application of standard methods of statistical inference to areal data can be rigorously justified (see, e.g., Stephan, 1934; Duncan and Duncan, 1957, Appendix H). Still another attitude taken by investigators toward this problem is that "regional differentiation" is to be assigned some (usually not too clearly specified) role in the explanation of areal variation. According to this view, areal units differ in their characteristics in part because they are located in different "regions."

There is no consensus of opinion as to how the degree of resemblance among neighboring areal units is to be measured, but a consideration of four alternative approaches may offer some insight into the nature of the problem.

(a) An approach that involves a rather artificial simplification of the problem can be illustrated with the following data. A systematic sample of 205 counties in the United States was selected. For each sample county a list was made of all counties bordering on it. In each case, one county was taken from the list at random, using random numbers. Data on certain variables were compiled for the 205 sample pairs of counties, and the intraclass correlation for each variable was computed with the results indicated in Table 3. (In a few cases, a given county appeared more than once, e.g., as a neighbor of two different counties or once as a sample county and once as a neighbor.)

## Table 3

### Intraclass Correlations between Sample Pairs of Counties, for Selected Variables, United States: 1950

| Variable | Number of sample pairs* | Correlation |
|---|---|---|
| Per cent of land in farms | 205 | .75 |
| Per cent of farms tenant-operated | 205 | .80 |
| Median gross monthly rent, nonfarm dwelling units | 195 | .71 |
| Per cent of families with 1949 incomes under $2,000 | 197 | .78 |
| Per cent increase in population, 1940-50 | 205 | .36 |

\* Number varies because census data are not shown for certain counties with small frequencies.

The high intraclass correlations for four of the variables leave no doubt that adjacent counties resemble each other much more closely than would counties paired at random. Since these four variables are in no sense a sample of county characteristics, one cannot conclude, of course, that similar results would obtain for other variables, although it seems likely that high intraclass correlations would be found for many socio-economic characteristics. The comparatively low correlation for the fifth variable, rate of population growth, suggests that adjacent units may bear less resemblance in their rates of change than in respect to static characteristics; however, this suggestion requires more careful study to be worth much. The artificiality of this approach is evident from the way the sampling frame was set up. The probability of a county's appearing in the sample as a neighboring county depends on the number of counties bordering the one initially selected. More important, if a large number of counties were included in the sample, there would be a larger number of duplications—counties appearing in several pairs—and the meaning of the intraclass correlation as a descriptive statistic would become obscure.

(b) A more rigorous approach is that of Geary (1954), some portions of whose little-known paper we shall summarize here. Let $Y_i$ be an observation on variable $Y$ for the $i^{\text{th}}$ areal unit $(i = 1, \ldots, n)$. The contiguity ratio, $c$, is defined as follows:

$$c = \frac{\dfrac{1}{2\Sigma k_i} \sum_i \sum_{i \neq i'}^{*} (Y_i - Y_{i'})^2}{\dfrac{1}{n-1} \sum_i (Y_i - \bar{Y})^2},$$

where the notation $\Sigma^*$ means that the summation is over contiguous areal units (denoted by $i'$) only and where $k_i$ is the number of "connections" (i.e., contiguous areal units) for the $i^{\text{th}}$ areal unit. The denominator is an estimate of the universe variance on the viewpoint that the $Y_i$ are a random sample from a hypothetical universe of observations on the areal units. The numerator is a measure of the average dispersion of $Y$ within "clusters" of areal units, each cluster being defined by a given areal unit and all areal units contiguous thereto. The constants in the formula are selected so as to make the expected value of $c$ unity for a spatially random arrangement of areal units having the observed values of $Y$.

It may be noted that the contiguity ratio bears a general resemblance to the correlation ratio, which is mentioned subsequently as a measure of "regional differentiation." Its numerator depends on "within-cluster" variation. The expression for this variation is written in a somewhat unusual form involving squared differences between each pair of observations in the "cluster," rather than in terms of squared deviations from the cluster mean. However, there is a theorem which states that "the variance may . . . be defined as half the mean square of all possible variate differences, that is to say, without reference to deviations from a central value, the mean" (Kendall, 1947, p. 42). The contiguity ratio, then, takes the form of a ratio of "within" to "total" variation. The correlation ratio (squared) may be written as unity minus a ratio of "within" to "total" variation. Hence, as a descriptive statistic, $1 - c$ has a meaning analogous to that of the correlation ratio, except for the way "clusters" are defined.

For purposes of computation, the formula for $c$ can be simplified as follows:

$$c = \frac{n(n-1)}{\sum\limits_i k_i} \cdot \frac{\sum\limits_i k_i Y_i^2 - 2\sum\limits_i \sum\limits_{i<i'}{}^* Y_i Y_{i'}}{n\sum\limits_i Y_i^2 - (\sum\limits_i Y_i)^2}.$$

Geary considers the sampling distribution of $c$ from both the "randomization" and the "normal theory" points of view. Here we shall mention only the formulas used when it is assumed that the $Y_i$ are a sample from a normally distributed universe. In this case we have

$$\text{var}(c) = \frac{n-1}{n^2(n+1)K_1^2}\left\{n^2 K_1^2 + 2n(K_1 + K_2)\right\} - 1,$$

where

$$K_1 = \frac{\sum\limits_i k_i}{n},$$

$$K_2 = \frac{\sum\limits_i k_i^2}{n};$$

and the standard error is $SE(c) = \sqrt{var(c)}$. The quantity $R = (1 - c)/SE(c)$ is interpreted as a normal deviate to test the significance of the departure of the observed value of $c$ from unity. It will be noted that $SE(c)$ depends only on $n$ and the $k_i$; hence, it may be computed once and for all for use with any characteristic of the areal units, provided only that one may assume a normal distribution of the characteristic.

One type of application of the contiguity ratio is indicated by Geary (1954, pp. 124, 137) as follows,

The typical procedure would consist in first establishing by the c test that the original observations were contiguous. The regression between the original observations and a series of correlative observations would be determined by least square procedure. The remainders would then be tested for contiguity. If the original observations were highly contiguous and the remainders not significantly so, this might be a good test for the thesis that the independent variables completely "explain" the observations. . . . independent variables, even if highly correlated with the dependent variables, do not necessarily "explain" the contiguity of the latter.

The last sentence in this excerpt suggests that the author may have in mind a distinction between "explaining" the total variation in a dependent variable and "explaining" its contiguity. He does not elaborate such a distinction. However, it is interesting to see that he gives as an illustration of the indicated use of independent variables the following regression model:

$$Y_i = a + bX_{1i} + cX_{2i} + dX_{1i}^2 + eX_{2i}^2 + fX_{1i}X_{2i} + U_i,$$

where $Y_i$ is the value of the dependent variable observed for the $i$th areal unit, $X_{1i}$ is that unit's horizontal coordinate ("longitude"), $X_{2i}$ is its vertical co-ordinate ("latitude"), and $U_i$ is the error of the regression estimate for the $i^{th}$ areal unit. If one or more of the coefficients in this equation are significant, there is evidence of a tendency toward a fairly simple pattern of variation over space in the dependent variable. If the contiguity ratio computed for the $U_i$ does not differ significantly from unity, it may be said that this pattern "explains" the contiguity of the $Y_i$. However, one would doubtless hesitate to concede that such a model could "explain" areal differentiation in any substantive sense, even if all $U_i$ were zero. Geary's procedure here, in fact, is tantamount to fitting a surface to the observations in three dimensional $(Y, X_1, X_2)$ space. It is thus perfectly analogous to the procedure of removing trend by a mathematical formula in time series analysis and has no more fundamental justification. One could, of course, consider formulas other than Geary's, although his is flexible enough to represent a variety of fairly simple spatial patterns.

Geary also suggests that the $U_i$ be studied in connection with regression models incorporating socio-economic variables instead of spatial co-ordinates. If one were studying areal variation of mortality rates, for example, he would probably wish to remove variation in the rates attributable to areal differences in age composition and economic status before concluding that the rates differed in response to, say, environmental factors.

A simple illustration of the use of the contiguity ratio will be presented in order to lend some feeling of concreteness to the discussion. Infant mortality rates (deaths under one year of age per 1,000 live births) were ascertained for the forty-eight States for 1950. The positive skewness of the rates was reduced, though not eliminated, by taking as $Y$ the square root of the infant mortality rate. The computed value of $c$ was .6777. The standard error of $c$, on the assumption of normality, is a function only of the number of areal units and pattern of "connections." Contiguous States were identified from the convenient list given by Lee *et al.* (1957, Table P-3), and the standard error was computed as .1146. Hence $R$, for the infant mortality example, was 2.812, indicating highly significant contiguity. (Table 4 indicates the computations.) For illustration, the State median income in 1949 of families $(X_i)$, as reported in the 1950 Census, was taken as an independent variable. The linear regression was found to be $Y_i = 6.702 - .043478 X_i + U_i$, with the corresponding correlation coefficient $-.486$. The contiguity

### Table 4

### Portion of Worksheet for Computation of Contiguity Ratio for State Infant Mortality Rates (Square Root Transformation): 1950

| State $(i)$ and contiguous* States $(i')$ | Square root of infant mortality rate $Y_i$ | $Y_i'$ | Number of connections† $k_i$ | $k_i^2$ | Product $Y_i Y_i'$ $(i < i')$ | Square $Y_i^2$ | Weighted square $k_i Y_i^2$ |
|---|---|---|---|---|---|---|---|
| 1. Alabama | 6.07 | ... | 4 | 16 | ... | 36.8449 | 147.3796 |
| 8. Florida | ... | 5.67 | ... | ... | 34.4169 | ... | ... |
| 9. Georgia | ... | 5.79 | ... | ... | 35.1453 | ... | ... |
| 22. Mississippi | ... | 6.06 | ... | ... | 36.7842 | ... | ... |
| 40. Tennessee | ... | 6.03 | ... | ... | 36.6021 | ... | ... |
| . . . | . | . | . | . | . | . | . |
| 9. Georgia | 5.79 | ... | 5 | 25 | ... | 33.5241 | 167.6205 |
| 31. North Carolina | ... | 5.87 | ... | ... | 33.9873 | ... | ... |
| 38. South Carolina | ... | 6.21 | ... | ... | 35.9559 | ... | ... |
| 40. Tennessee | ... | 6.03 | ... | ... | 34.9137 | ... | ... |
| . . . | . | . | . | . | . | . | . |
| 44. Virginia | 5.88 | ... | 5 | 25 | ... | 34.5744 | 172.8720 |
| 46. West Virginia | ... | 6.01 | ... | ... | 35.3388 | ... | ... |

* List only states with a serial number greater than *i*.
† Contiguous states.

ratio for the $U_i$ is .8781, with the corresponding value of $R$, 1.064, indicating a nonsignificant departure of $c$ from unity. Apparently State differences in income "explain" the contiguity of State infant mortality rates, although less than a fourth (the square of .486 is .236) of the total State variation in infant mortality rates is "explained" by their regression on State median family income.

Figure V provides a rough basis for visualizing the results of the foregoing illustrative analysis. Figure VA shows the observed infant mortality rates, with the States grouped into quartiles. In Figure VB the quartile grouping is based on residuals from the regression line. It may be observed that eighteen States shifted from one quartile position to another. The differing degree of contiguity in the two maps is perhaps obvious at a glance. However, it is also easy to count the number of instances of individual States not contiguous to another in the same quartile: seven on the basis of the observed data, fifteen on the basis of deviations from the regression line. Although the formal test of the contiguity coefficient yields a non-significant result for the data of Figure VB, the eye detects certain large "clusters" of States falling in the same quartile. In an actual study, therefore, one might wish to investigate alternative independent variables or combinations thereof to see which ones are most successful in removing the contiguity.

(c) Another approach to the contiguity problem is the grouping of areal units into regions, i.e., sets of contiguous areal units. For the moment we are not concerned with the principles on which such a grouping is accomplished or with what kinds of information are to be considered relevant to a choice among alternative groupings. Given such a regional grouping, regional differentiation is evidenced by the finding that areal units in the same region resemble each other to a greater degree than would areal units grouped at random and, specifically, without reference to their spatial contiguity.

The use of the correlation ratio as a measure of regional differentiation is suggested if one takes a conventional regression approach to the analysis of the relationship between two areally differentiated variables. Let $(X_{ij}, Y_{ij})$ be a bivariate observation on the $i^{th}$ areal unit in the $j^{th}$ region. Then it can be shown, using the same reasoning as that employed in section 3.1, that

$$r_T = r_w \sqrt{1 - E_{YR}^2} \sqrt{1 - E_{XR}^2} + r_b E_{YR} E_{XR},$$

where $r_T$ is the total correlation between $Y$ and $X$, $r_w$ is the average within-region correlation, $r_b$ is the between-region correlation, and $E_{YR}^2$ and $E_{XR}^2$ are the squared correlation ratios of the two variables on region, i.e., ratios of the respective between-region to total sums of squares. Similarly it can be shown that

$$b_T = b_w + E_{XR}^2 (b_b - b_w),$$

where the subscripts of the regression coefficients have the same meaning as the corresponding ones of the correlation coefficients. These relationships are deduced on the assumption that each areal unit is given equal weight rather than a weight proportional to its size.

The general similarity between what Geary calls the "contiguity effect" and what is here treated as "regional differentiation" suggests the plausibility of a parallel approach to the handling of regression in which the regional differentiation of $Y$ is determined initially; then the remainders of $Y$ from its regression on one or more independent variables are analyzed for regional differentiation. In the two-variable case, using linear regression, we would have the regression model,

Figure V. *Infant Mortality Rates, by States, United States: 1950.*

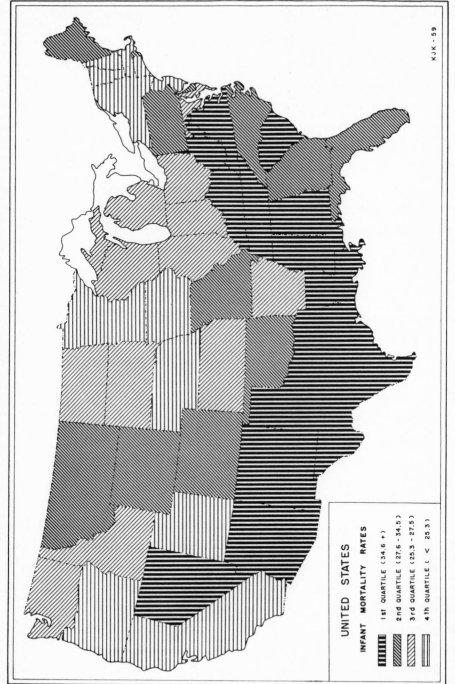

KJK - 59

UNITED STATES

INFANT MORTALITY RATES

| | 1st QUARTILE ( 34.6 + ) |
| | 2nd QUARTILE ( 27.6 - 34.5 ) |
| | 3rd QUARTILE ( 25.3 - 27.5 ) |
| | 4th QUARTILE ( < 25.3 ) |

A. *States grouped into quartiles on the basis of observed infant mortality rates.*

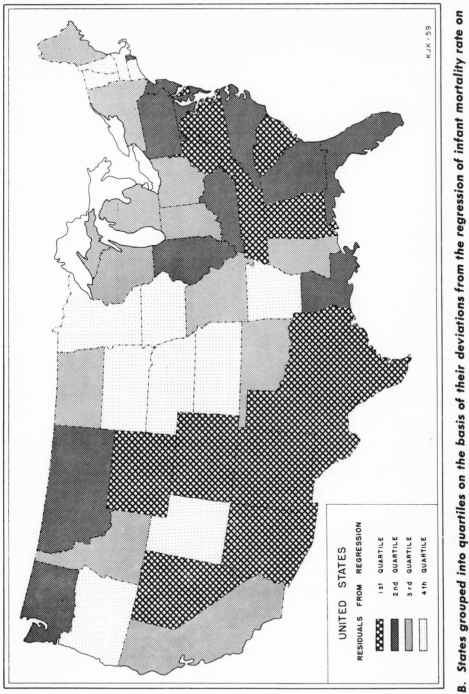

KJK-59

UNITED STATES

RESIDUALS FROM REGRESSION

1st QUARTILE
2nd QUARTILE
3rd QUARTILE
4th QUARTILE

B. *States grouped into quartiles on the basis of their deviations from the regression of infant mortality rate on 1949 median family income.*

$$Y_{ij} = a + b_T X_{ij} + U_{ij},$$

and we would be comparing $E_{YR}^2$, the regional differentiation of the $Y$'s, with $E_{UR}^2$, the regional differentiation of the residuals from the total regression of $Y$ on $X$. It can be shown that

$$E_{UR}^2 = \frac{E_{YR}^2 + r_T^2 E_{XR}^2 - 2 r_T r_b E_{YR} E_{XR}}{1 - r_T^2}.$$

Hence the regional differentiation of the residuals can be ascertained without actually calculating each residual.

Whereas Geary offers a significance test for the contiguity ratio of both the original observations and the remainders from the regression, we are not quite sure what test of significance is appropriate for $E_{UR}^2$. The usual approach for testing whether $E_{YR}^2$ departs significantly from zero is to use the $F$-test for a one-criterion analysis of variance with degrees of freedom $n_1 = k - 1$ and $n_2 = N - k$, where there are $N$ areal units grouped into $k$ regions. It is easy to show, in fact, that

$$E^2 = \frac{F(k-1)}{F(k-1) + N - k}.$$

One would be tempted similarly to use the $F$-test in connection with an analysis of variance of the residuals (the $U$'s), with an adjustment of degrees of freedom for the number of independent variables in the regression. However, so far as we know, this procedure has no rigorous justification.

(d) At the outset of this section we mentioned that some investigators think of regional differentiation as playing a role in the explanation of areal variation. In our opinion, this view is to be accepted only with grave reservations. In common parlance, of course, we talk as if "regions" constitute an influence on social and economic phenomena. If we are told that wages are low in the textile industry we are likely to "explain" this observation by referring to the concentration of that industry in the South. But on further reflection we see that this merely tells us *where* wages are low, not *why* they are low. To be sure, "the South" may stand as a sort of shorthand expression for a lot of reasons for low wages, and if we have actually investigated these reasons and established their validity, there is no particular harm in an elliptical allusion to the "region" where the combination of influences on wages is particularly unfavorable. But if the actual reasons for low wages are poorly understood, the remark that they are characteristic of the South is only a pseudo-explanation, at best a clue to the discovery of these reasons—a clue which may or may not be of some heuristic value for an investigator familiar with conditions prevailing in the region.

We shall present an exposition of the way in which regional classification is sometimes used as an explanatory variable, returning for an example to the regression of infant mortality on income and using the square root transformation of the infant mortality rate. As was indicated, the regression of the square root of the infant mortality rate $(Y)$ on 1949 median family income in hundreds of dollars $(X)$ for the forty-eight States, was found to be $\hat{Y} = 6.702 - .04378\,X$, and the correlation between $Y$ and $X$ is $-.486$. Now, if we compute the average within-region regression coefficient, $b_w$, we may use the following equation to estimate $Y$ from $X$:

$$\hat{Y}_{ij} = \bar{Y}_j - b_w \bar{X}_j + b_w X_{ij},$$

where $\bar{Y}_j$ and $\bar{X}_j$ are the regional means of the dependent and the independent variable, respectively. We are using the notation already introduced, letting $(X_{ij}, Y_{ij})$ be a bivariate observation on the $i^{th}$ areal unit in the $j^{th}$ region. (This notation, which is very convenient for discussing analysis of covariance, is a slight modification of that used by Walker and Lev, 1953, Chapter 15.) For the present illustration, we have employed the four regions recognized by the Bureau of the Census. The within-region regressions for this model are as follows:

| Northeast | $\hat{Y} = 6.232 - 0.03738\,X$ |
| North Central | $\hat{Y} = 6.277 - 0.03738\,X$ |
| South | $\hat{Y} = 6.640 - 0.03738\,X$ |
| West | $\hat{Y} = 6.879 - 0.03738\,X.$ |

It is helpful to note that these results may be written in the form of a single multiple regression equation, using dummy variables for regions (Suits, 1957). We then have

$$\hat{Y} = 6.640 - 0.03738\,X - 0.408\,R_1 - 0.363\,R_2 + 0.239\,R_3,$$

where the dummy variable $R_1$ is scored 1 if the State falls in the Northeast region and 0 if it does not, $R_2$ is 1 for a State in the North Central region and 0 for any other State, and $R_3$ is 1 for a State in the West and 0 for any other State. (Note that only three of the four regions enter as dummy variables, for if a State is not in the Northeast, North Central, or West, it must be in the South; which of the regions is left out is immaterial.) We may therefore think of the result obtained from the analysis of covariance approach in terms of the average within-region regression as yielding a multiple regression of $Y$ on $X$ and region. The multiple correlation corresponding to this regression equation is .664, considerably higher in absolute value than the zero-order total correlation, $-.486$, between $Y$ and $X$.

The foregoing procedure is justified, according to the theory of analysis of covariance, if in fact the regression coefficients for the several regions are not significantly different. That theory provides a significance test suitable for making a decision on this point (see Walker and Lev, 1953, Chapter 15). If the regressions within regions do differ significantly, then the investigator may wish to combine his information on the independent variable and region to estimate the dependent variable by calculating the individual within-region regressions. For our illustration, such a calculation yields the following results:

| Northeast | $\hat{Y} = 6.099 - 0.03317\,X$ |
| North Central | $\hat{Y} = 5.478 - 0.01161\,X$ |
| South | $\hat{Y} = 6.203 - 0.01778\,X$ |
| West | $\hat{Y} = 11.480 - 0.17835\,X.$ |

As before, we may think of these results in terms of a multiple regression of $Y$ on $X$ and region, which is of the following form:

$$\hat{Y} = 6.203 - 0.01778\,X - 0.104\,R_1 - 0.725\,R_2 + 5.277\,R_3$$
$$- 0.01539\,XR_1 + 0.00617\,XR_2 - 0.16057\,XR_3,$$

where the dummy variables are the same as before. The appearance of the product terms, $XR_1$ etc., in the equation signifies that there is an "interaction" between the independent variable and region (Suits, 1957). The correlation coefficient corresponding to this multiple regression is .764, appreciably higher than that obtained by the covariance model. It must be remembered, of course, that the computation of this correlation uses up more degrees of freedom than does that obtained by the covariance model, which, in turn, uses up more degrees of freedom than does the computation of the total zero-order correlation. If the analysis of covariance shows that the within-region regression coefficients differ non-significantly, then the increment in the multiple correlation would, of course, be non-significant.

The relationships among the three correlation coefficients are clarified by considering the components of the sum of squares of $Y$ about the total regression line of $Y$ on $X$. Let $S_T$ be the total sum of squares of observations about the regression line for all areal units; let $S_2$ be the sum of squares of observations about the respective individual within-region regression lines; let $S_w$ be the sum of squares of observations about the within-region regression lines with common slope $b_w$; and let $S_b$ be the sum of squares of region means about the regression line with slope $b_w$. Then it can be shown that $S_T = S_w + S_b$, and $S_T \geqslant S_w \geqslant S_2$ (Walker and Lev, 1953, Chapter 15). The three correlations just referred to can be written with expressions that are quite similar in form: the total zero-order correlation,

$$r = \sqrt{1 - \frac{S_T}{C_{yyT}}};$$

the multiple correlation for the covariance model,

$$r' = \sqrt{1 - \frac{S_w}{C_{yyT}}};$$

and the multiple correlation for the model using individual within-region regressions,

$$r'' = \sqrt{1 - \frac{S_2}{C_{yyT}}}.$$

Whence it follows that $r'' \geqslant r' \geqslant r$. One must, of course, bear in mind that these coefficients have different numbers of degrees of freedom. Where there are $N$ areal units in $k$ regions, the degrees of freedom are $N - 2$ for $r$, $N - k - 1$ for $r'$, and $N - 2k$ for $r''$. Ezekiel (1941, pp. 142 and 208-211) suggests that correlation coefficients be adjusted for degrees of freedom by the formula,

$$\bar{r}^2 = 1 - \frac{(1 - r^2)(N - 1)}{N - m},$$

where $\bar{r}$ is the adjusted correlation and $m$ is the number of constants in the multiple regression equation. We therefore have, for the three correlations in our preceding examples, the following values:

|  | $r$ | $\bar{r}$ |
|---|---|---|
| Zero-order total correlation | −.486 | −.469 |
| Covariance model, with common slope $b_w$ | .664 | .624 |
| Individual within-region regression model | .764 | .714 |

The investigator should, therefore, be aware that in introducing even a gross regional classification of areal units as an explanatory variable, he is using up degrees of freedom more rapidly than he would, say, by adding another quantitative independent variable to his regression equation.

What is sometimes referred to as the "regional effect" seemingly has one or both of two meanings. First, the finding of a "regional effect" may be based on the observation that regional means of the dependent variable differ significantly. The magnitude of the "regional effect" may be measured by the correlation ratio of the dependent variable on region (see e.g., Varley, 1956). Such an "effect" may appear prior to any regression analysis, or it may persist after the influence of one or more independent variables have been eliminated by the methods of analysis of covariance. Second, the term "regional effect" may be used to indicate the finding that the within-region regressions have significantly different slopes, i.e., that the relation between the dependent and independent variables differs from one region to another (Maitland and Fisher, 1958, pp. 24-28). It should be carefully observed that the appearance of either type of "regional effect" depends a good deal on how the regions are delimited (Duncan and Cuzzort, 1958). The investigator employing "region" as an explanatory factor and assigning substantive importance to the observation of a "regional effect" will be in one of two positions in regard to the delimitation of regions. Either he will be using a "ready-made" set of regions, or he will have delimited a special set for his own study. In the first case, he has the problem of choosing which of a number of alternative ready-made sets he will use, and he can well anticipate that his "regional effects" will be different if he uses one rather than another. In respect to the second case, it is commonly said that a set of regions should be "tailor-made" for each study, but the advocates of this point of view have never made clear what pattern should be used to cut the cloth in order to get the best results, or even what would constitute such optimum results. There are, of course, numerous discussions of methods for delimiting regions. But none of them is explicitly oriented to the problem of using regions as explanatory factors after the fashion of our foregoing examples.

We conclude that the situation in regard to the use of "region" as an explanatory factor is, at best, obscure, unless one simply chooses to follow out a computing routine more or less mechanically, without regard to the meaning of the results. In fact, there is much to be said for the view that using "region" to "explain" areal variation merely signifies that the investigator has not finished his problem. On the other hand, the existence of contiguity or regional effects in the residuals from regressions or other explanatory models in which "region" is not an explanatory factor explicitly is prima facie evidence of incompleteness in the system of explanatory variables. As Simon (1957, Chapter 2) points out, in a rigorous attempt to distinguish genuine from spurious correlation we must make "*a priori* assumptions that the errors are uncorrelated—i.e., that 'all other' variables influencing *x* are uncorrelated with 'all other' variables influencing *y,* and so on." Spatial, as well as temporal, "clumping" of the data would seem to be a sign of what the econometrician calls "errors in the equations" due to omitted variables, and, consequently, of the likelihood that introducing additional variables would change the apparent influence of certain of the explanatory factors.

Much of the foregoing material has implications for the concept of "region" as it has figured in theoretical discussion and empirical research on areal differentiation. We are often told that if investigators would delimit "their regions, *giving due cognizance to the objective of the research and the best possible criteria,* then they could proceed with their regional analysis secure in the thought that their studies were based on the most rational choice of regions" (Thomas, 1958, p. 200; italics in original). Unfortunately, what the "best possible criteria" may be remains obscure, despite the considerable amount of discussion that has been devoted to the topic (see, e.g., James and Jones, 1954, Chapter 2; Isard, 1956; Perloff, 1957). Moreover, it would appear that the most sophisticated statistical methods of regional delimitation (e.g., Berry, 1958; Bogue, 1951; Hagood, 1943) have been used to produce general-purpose regions rather than regions "giving due cognizance" to the objectives of particular studies. We believe that some light is shed on the problem by considering the meaning that the notion of "region" might have in the context of a discussion of the explanation of areal variation.

We discuss only the case in which a region (often called a "homogeneous region") is constructed as a cluster or composite of more elementary areal units on the basis of the similarity of the units in the cluster and their proximity in space. This is the case, for example, when counties are combined into State Economic Areas; or when States are combined into Census geographic divisions. It is assumed, in any given instance, that the elementary areal unit is spatially indivisible, i.e., that information on spatial variation *within* elementary areal units is unavailable or is disregarded. Ordinarily the indicators of similarity of elementary areal units will be statistics such as percentages, ratios, averages, or index numbers based on quantitative data for each unit. However, the notion of similarity includes the case when two or more units fall into the same category of a dichotomy or manifold classification.

Excluded from this discussion is the case in which regions are delimited without reference to any pre-existing areal units and without recourse to tabulations of data for such units taken as building blocks. For example, a river-basin region may be delimited by observing in the field where there is a divide between the given basin and others. In principle, such a boundary for a region is uniquely determined, although in practice, of course, it can only be located approximately, and the approximation may, for reasons of convenience, be made to coincide with boundaries of established areal units. As another example, regional boundaries might be drawn along lines of equal population potential. Again, the boundary in principle is uniquely determined with mathematical precision, aside from approximations due to errors of measurement and those accepted as a matter of expediency.

The distinction between these two types of regional delimitation is reminiscent of the distinction between "isopleth" and "isometric" lines used in cartography (Schmid and MacCannell, 1955, p. 200).

> The term "isopleth" . . . designates one of two types of isoline maps in which the lines (isopleths) connect equal rates or ratios for specific areas. In the other type of isoline map, which is commonly referred to as an isometric map, lines (isometers) are drawn through points of equal value or intensity. In the "isopleth" map, the values are rates or ratios computed for areal units . . . [;] whereas in the "isometric" map the values are samples of absolute measurement taken at different points on a map. A population density map with lines showing equal densities is an example of the "isopleth" map, and a topographic map with lines connecting a series of points of equal elevation . . . is an example of the "isometric" map.

The boundaries of the kind of region discussed here are, of course, "isopleths" only to a gross approximation, unless they have been generalized for purposes of cartographic representation. This is necessarily the case for any use of regions in statistical analysis since, by supposition, data are not available for subdivisions of the elementary areal units. Moreover, to respect principles of spatial clustering or proximity, it may be necessary to include in a region one or more elementary areal units whose statistical values fall outside the interval that would be used in constructing an isopleth map. For example, a State Economic Area comprising counties with generally "low" values of an indicator may contain an isolated county with a "high" value, simply because such a county cannot be assigned to another SEA.

A second important limitation on the scope of this discussion is the exclusion of considerations that arise from the use of "regions" for merely descriptive or impressionistic purposes or from extra-scientific uses such as appreciation of regional distinctiveness. Our framework is, explicitly, that of the *statistical explanation of areal variation.* More fully: We are given a universe of territory subdivided into elementary areal units subject to variation in several (quantitative or qualitative) aspects; one such aspect is taken as a "dependent variable" and an empirical model explaining variation in this dependent variable is to be constructed, utilizing information on one or more "explanatory variables," or other aspects of the elementary areal units. The model of multiple linear regression may be kept in mind as the type case of statistical explanation, although other modes of analysis may be employed. Our discussion, then, concerns the question of how the notion of region may arise in connection with the statistical analysis of areal variation.

To present the matter in as elementary a fashion as possible, we consider a comparison of just two areal units, raising the question of whether they belong in the same or in different regions. Certain basic criteria of belonging together in the same region may be entertained. For example, do we require that the two areal units—let us designate them $A$ and $B$—be contiguous or at least relatively close to one another in space? Since $A$ and $B$ may be alike or different from each other in respect to a variable $Y$, the explanation of areal variation in which is the focus of a study, do we require similarity on this "dependent" variable as a condition for including $A$ and $B$ in the same region? Given a set of explanatory variables, $X_1, X_2, X_3, \ldots X_m$, which is supposed to account for the areal variation in $Y$ to some significant degree, do we require that $A$ and $B$ exhibit similar values on each of the $X_i$ or merely that $A$ and $B$ be similar on $\hat{Y}$, which is the weighted sum of the $X_i$, the weights being determined by regression analysis; or may we disregard entirely the determinants of $Y$ in assigning $A$ and $B$ to regions? The conjunction of the alternatives suggested by such criteria gives rise to a number of logical possibilities. These had best be set down in systematic fashion to avoid unnecessary confusion. To simplify consideration of the situation, we assume that comparisons of $A$ and $B$ can be expressed with sufficient precision in terms of a dichotomy: their values on a specified variable are either "similar" or "different."

Table 5 sets forth a framework of categories in which areal units $A$ and $B$ may be compared according to criteria like those just suggested. We are given that each areal unit has associated with it a value of a dependent variable, $Y$. A regression equation to estimate $Y$ is computed so that the calculated or estimated value of $Y$, $\hat{Y} = f(X_1, X_2, \ldots X_m)$. If for any areal unit the discrepancy, $Y - \hat{Y}$, is smaller than an arbitrary number, the estimate from the regression equation is considered "accurate"; otherwise, it is "inaccurate." Given any two areal units, $A$ and $B$, occurring in the universe of territory, they may be described as "adjacent or in the same vicinity" if they are in spatial proximity; otherwise they are considered "not adjacent or close together." (It is recognized that a quantitative judgment of degree of proximity may be difficult in certain cases; but these particular difficulties are not in principle relevant to the discussion here.) If for the two areal units, $A$ and $B$, $Y_a - Y_b$ is "small" in absolute value, the two units are said to be "similar" on the dependent variable; otherwise, they are "different." In like fashion the comparison between the estimated values $\hat{Y}_a$ and $\hat{Y}_b$ may reveal the two to be "similar" or "different." Finally, two areal units, $A$ and $B$, are said to be "similar" on their profiles of independent variables if for each $X_i$ in the set $(X_1 \ldots X_m)$ the difference $X_{ia} - X_{ib}$ is "small" in absolute value; otherwise the two are "different" in their profiles. (In judging whether differences are sufficiently "small," one might express variate values in standard

## Table 5

### Framework for Comparing Two Areal Units, A and B, on Characteristics Relevant to their Regional Classification

| Location of A and B | Estimated ($\hat{Y}$) and observed ($Y$) values of dependent variable | Profile of values on explanatory variables ($X_i$) | |
|---|---|---|---|
| | | Accuracy of regression estimate | |
| | | A similar to B | A different from B |
| A and B adjacent or in the same vicinity | $\hat{Y}_a$ similar to $\hat{Y}_b$ and $Y_a$ similar to $Y_b$ | (1) i. Accurate for both A and B  ii. Inaccurate for both A and B | (2) i. Accurate for both A and B  ii. Inaccurate for both A and B |
| | $\hat{Y}_a$ similar to $\hat{Y}_b$ but $Y_a$ differs from $Y_b$ | (3) i. Accurate for either A or B  ii. Inaccurate for both A and B | (4) i. Accurate for either A or B  ii. Inaccurate for both A and B |
| | $\hat{Y}_a$ differs from $\hat{Y}_b$ but $Y_a$ similar to $Y_b$ | — | (5) i. Accurate for either A or B  ii. Inaccurate for both A and B |
| | $\hat{Y}_a$ differs from $\hat{Y}_b$ and $Y_a$ differs from $Y_b$ | — | (6) i. Accurate for both A and B  ii. Accurate for either A or B  iii. Inaccurate for both A and B |

| A and B not adjacent or in the same vicinity | | |
|---|---|---|
| $\hat{Y}_a$ similar to $\hat{Y}_b$ and $Y_a$ similar to $Y_b$ | **(7)** i. Accurate for both A and B  ii. Inaccurate for both A and B | **(8)** i. Accurate for both A and B  ii. Inaccurate for both A and B |
| $\hat{Y}_a$ similar to $\hat{Y}_b$ but $Y_a$ differs from $Y_b$ | **(9)** i. Accurate for either A or B  ii. Inaccurate for both A and B | **(10)** i. Accurate for either A or B  ii. Inaccurate for both A and B |
| $\hat{Y}_a$ differs from $\hat{Y}_b$ but $Y_a$ similar to $Y_b$ | — | **(11)** i. Accurate for either A or B  ii. Inaccurate for both A and B |
| $\hat{Y}_a$ differs from $\hat{Y}_b$ and $Y_a$ differs from $Y_b$ | — | **(12)** i. Accurate for both A and B  ii. Accurate for either A or B  iii. Inaccurate for both A and B |

form, i.e., as deviations from the mean in ratio to the standard deviation. Moreover, one might be prepared to ignore greater differences for a variable whose weight in the regression equation is low than for one whose weight is high.)

The several dimensions represented in Table 5 are not logically independent; hence a number of cells in the complete cross-classification are not represented in the framework. For example, if the profiles of independent variables of $A$ and $B$ are "similar," their estimated dependent variables must be "similar" too. Consequently, the combination "Profile similar, $\hat{Y}$ different" cannot occur.

To give the reader a concrete feeling for the kinds of comparisons that may occur, Table 6 provides illustrations of several of the possibilities of Table 5 taken from an actual analysis of the areal variation in a dependent variable. (These data are taken from a study reported in B. Duncan, 1957.) In these illustrations the elementary areal units are State Economic Areas (SEA's). As an example, consider SEA's Nebraska-6 and South Dakota-4a. The two are quite similar in terms of the dependent variable, per cent of land in farms, the respective values being 96 and 97. They are similar, as well, in the values estimated from the regression equation involving four independent variables, the respective $\hat{Y}$'s being 97 and 98 per cent. In both cases the estimate from the regression equation may be considered quite "accurate." Moreover, as the tabulation in Table 6 shows, the two SEA's have quite "similar" profiles on the four independent variables.

Employing the numbered categories or cells of Table 5, we may now elucidate several notions about regions.

The most rudimentary conception of a "homogeneous region" is perhaps that of the "simple one-factor region." For convenience, let the factor in question be the one here identified as the dependent variable, $Y$. Areal units similar in $Y$, if they are in spatial proximity, are grouped together as a region. A familiar example is that of the "corn belt" in the north central United States, which is a grouping (usually of counties) that are high on some indicator of corn production. The aggregate of the comparisons represented by cells 1, 2, and 5 corresponds to this conception of a region. It is worth noting that a simple region constructed from the evidence of one variable alone may be heterogeneous with respect to other pertinent variables. If the explanatory model is a relatively successful one, much of the variation in $Y$ can be "explained" by the independent variables. In such a case two areal units similar in $Y$ would be alike for the same "reasons" if their comparison fell in cell 1, but for different "reasons" if it fell in cell 2. Hypothetically, of two counties in the corn belt, one might have a high value of agricultural products because of proximity to a market; while for the other the critical factor might be a favorable combination of natural resources. The example previously cited (SEA's Nebraska-6 and South Dakota-4a) is one where the two units are alike for the same reasons and the comparison of Ohio-6a and Texas-3, Table 6, example for cell 8(i), is a case of two areal units being alike for different reasons.

Akin to the idea of a simple one-factor region is that of a one-factor stratum as encountered in the theory of stratified sampling; the difference is that areal units in a stratum (other than a regional stratum) need not be in the same vicinity. In addition to the cells already listed, a stratum would include cells 7, 8, and 11, i.e., all areal units similar on variable $Y$, irrespective of location with reference to each other. A simple example is the stratification of SEA's into metropolitan and non-

## Table 6

### Illustrative Comparisons of Areal Units

| Cell in Table 5 being illustrated | Pair of State Economic Areas | Variable* | | | | | |
|---|---|---|---|---|---|---|---|
| | | Y | $\hat{Y}$ | $X_1$ | $X_2$ | $X_3$ | $X_4$ |
| 1 (i) | Nebraska—6 | 96 | 97 | 24 | 16 | 28 | 120 |
| | S. Dakota—4a | 97 | 98 | 21 | 22 | 28 | 118 |
| 1 (ii) | California—9 | 18 | 37 | 14 | 18 | 31 | 4 |
| | Oregon—1b | 17 | 36 | 12 | 22 | 32 | 0 |
| 3 (i) | Kentucky—9 | 43 | 51 | 37 | 19 | 26 | 0 |
| | Tennessee—6 | 77 | 51 | 35 | 18 | 23 | 2 |
| 5 (i) | Mississippi—2 | 84 | 76 | 30 | 20 | 21 | 58 |
| | Mississippi—5 | 81 | 51 | 30 | 20 | 33 | 12 |
| 6 (i) | New York—3b | 69 | 69 | 42 | 18 | 43 | 45 |
| | Pennsylvania—2 | 58 | 52 | 42 | 17 | 27 | 0 |
| 7 (i) | South Dakota—4a | 97 | 98 | 21 | 22 | 28 | 118 |
| | Texas—6b | 93 | 96 | 21 | 20 | 29 | 116 |
| 7 (ii) | New York—7 | 43 | 67 | 32 | 19 | 36 | 47 |
| | North Carolina—11 | 41 | 66 | 28 | 20 | 31 | 45 |
| 8 (i) | Ohio—6a | 88 | 87 | 47 | 16 | 40 | 77 |
| | Texas—3 | 88 | 88 | 16 | 20 | 51 | 118 |
| 8 (ii) | Maine—2 | 15 | 44 | 22 | 21 | 36 | 7 |
| | Washington—4 | 16 | 45 | 13 | 16 | 35 | 28 |
| 10 (i) | Connecticut—1 | 44 | 51 | 54 | 14 | 48 | 0 |
| | Montana—2a | 77 | 50 | 13 | 25 | 43 | 30 |
| 11 (ii) | Michigan—6b | 78 | 92 | 43 | 16 | 35 | 90 |
| | Montana—2a | 77 | 50 | 13 | 25 | 43 | 30 |
| 12 (iii) | California—9 | 18 | 37 | 14 | 18 | 31 | 4 |
| | Tennessee—6 | 77 | 51 | 35 | 18 | 23 | 2 |

| *List of Variables | Mean | Standard Deviation |
|---|---|---|
| Y = per cent of land in farms | 68 | 24 |
| $X_1$ = population potential | 29 | 11 |
| $X_2$ = distance to metropolitan area | 18 | 3 |
| $X_3$ = index of urbanization | 33 | 8 |
| $X_4$ = index of soil quality | 52 | 37 |

$$Y = 24.33 + 0.590X_1 + 0.629X_2 - 0.284X_3 + 0.472X_4$$
(multiple correlation = .72).

metropolitan strata, where the variable takes a dichotomous form, based on presence or absence of a population center of a designated minimum size. (A corresponding type of region is sometimes recognized as a "metropolitan belt" of continuous metropolitan areas.)

Ordinarily, regions are constructed not on the basis of similarity in a single factor only, but in terms of multi-factor relative homogeneity. An outstanding example is Bogue's (1951) delimitation of State Economic Areas, taking counties as the elementary areal units. Bogue's procedure involved, among other things, examination of a considerable number of statistical indicators characterizing counties and the "regional" grouping of counties in spatial proximity according to their similarity on this battery of indicators. There is nothing in the published description of Bogue's procedure to indicate that any particular variable was regarded as the dependent variable; indeed, the delimitation of SEA's as general-purpose regions seems inconsistent with special emphasis on any single variable. Consequently, we may regard SEA's as "regions" evidencing, insofar as possible, similarity with respect to a profile of independent variables, but with the dependent variable unspecified. We may therefore think of SEA's as representing a type produced by the combination of cells 1 and 3 in Table 5.

Analogous to this type of "region"—but more general, in that it comprises cells 7 and 9 in addition to 1 and 3—would be a stratification of areal units according to two or more criteria of stratification. This could be accomplished by successive subclassification of areal units by a sequence of variables. An alternative procedure, described by Hagood and Bernert (1945), is to work out a composite index of the stratification variables and to group areas according to similarity on the composite variable. A generally similar technique of grouping areal units, disregarding spatial proximity, has been popularized by some sociologists studying intra-urban areas under the heading of "social areas" —a label that is probably as productive of confusion as of enlightenment (Shevky and Bell, 1955).

"Regions" devised for special studies, rather than for a range of general uses, may be delimited with explicit attention to a particular dependent variable, or class of dependent variables, along with variables considered to produce variation in the dependent variable. An example is the set of "productivity regions" devised for a study of resource productivity on farms (Strand and Heady, 1955, p. 10),

> . . . farms are grouped by regions within which agricultural resources and farming conditions and practices are relatively uniform. Regions . . . were outlined . . . on the basis of internal homogeneity in factors that affect or reflect the productivity of farm labor and other resources used in agriculture. . . . an effort was made to group all State economic areas into a limited number of productivity regions showing relatively great differences in productivity or production conditions, or both.

The elementary areal units in this example are SEA's; the regional groupings thereof being termed "productivity regions." The reference to factors that "affect or reflect" productivity implies an attempt to group areal units according to similarity in both the dependent variable (factors "reflecting" productivity) and the independent variables (factors "affecting" productivity). This general type of region falls in cell 1 of Table 5. An analogous type of stratum would include cells 1 and 7. Oftentimes, of course, the dependent variable is unknown in stratified sampling, the purpose of the sample being to ascertain its values; but the most effective type of stratification is that produced by a set of independent variables having a high relationship with the dependent variable.

It may be of some interest to compare briefly the framework offered here with a somewhat less operational conception of "region." A committee of geographers set forth the following (much abridged and rearranged) notion of a "homogeneous region" (James and Jones, 1954, pp. 32-33, 38),

> The region, in the technical sense proposed in this chapter, is an area in which accordant areal relations produce some form of cohesion. It is defined by specific criteria and is homogeneous only in terms of these criteria. . . . The region incorporates an association of coherent features. . . . Areas homogeneous in terms of single features are to be considered as regions only when they are shown to possess areal qualities accordant with one or more other regional systems. . . . an investigation which is successful in identifying and presenting regions must seek meaningful patterns, and should contain the demonstration that the patterns presented are, in fact, significant. . . . In geographic study a homogeneous area has meaning when it can be shown to correspond or coincide in its position on the earth with other homogeneous areas. But the identification of an accordant relationship . . . does not prove a causal relationship. The regional pattern has both meaning and significance when it can be interpreted in terms of systematically related processes, operating through time.

This statement seems to be, in the main, a general specification for the type of region of which "productivity regions" are an example. That is, to meet the geographers' criteria, a region would have to be not only homogeneous in the dependent variable, but also in a set of independent variables; and the dependent variable should be highly correlated with the combination of independent variables. Finally, the independent variables must not only estimate the dependent variable with considerable accuracy, but they must be variables to which "causal" or theoretical significance can be attributed. A clarification of geographic methodology might well result from the substitution of operational or statistical language (e.g., "variable," "correlation," "estimation," etc.) for somewhat vague concepts like "cohesion," "accordant," "meaning," etc.

## 3.6. Temporal Aspects of Areal Variation

In studies of areal distributions, spatial structure, and areal variation, the investigator often is as interested in the changes revealed by areal data in time series as he is in the pattern or structure that can be discerned at a given point in time. Indeed, some social scientists (e.g., Simiand, 1932, pp. 69-79, 105-10, 282-87) believe that genuine causal knowledge can be established only on the basis of longitudinal or diachronic observations, or at least by using information on the temporal relationships among variables. The need to understand the course of change and to forecast the direction of future change often is felt to be so great that the research worker is constrained to make some inference about change even though he lacks time series data. Thus the tacit assumption frequently is made that temporal relationships can be surmised from relationships holding in cross-sectional data. For example, we note that within most countries, urban populations at any given moment of time have lower fertility than rural populations; from this we go on to hypothesize that as a country becomes more urban, the fertility of its population is likely to decline.

It should be observed, however, that relationships inferred from cross-sectional data may sometimes be of little value in estimating or predicting changes over time. It is not difficult to point to instances in which this mode of reasoning fails. Inasmuch as Negroes are below whites in educational attainment;

one would assume that when Negroes replace white residents in an urban neighborhood, the neighborhood's average educational level will fall. But this need not occur if the incoming population is younger than the one displaced, because educational levels for both races have been rising over time (Duncan and Duncan, 1957, Chapter 7). Studies of the levels of living of farm operators indicate a high positive cross-sectional relationship between the per cent of farms having tractors in an area and the average level of living of farm operators. This would suggest that areas having the greatest increase in per cent of farms reporting tractors would also have the greatest increase in average level of living. This is not, however, the case. These two variables correlated .76 and .74 on the basis of cross-sectional data for State Economic Areas in 1930 and 1954, respectively. Nonetheless, the correlation between measures of change in the two variables from 1930 to 1954 was a nonsignificant .04 (Duncan and Cuzzort, 1958; the measure of change used in this study was "deviational change," defined below).

When cross-sectional and longitudinal approaches give seemingly contrary results, the investigator is faced with a problem of interpretation. We are unable to suggest a general strategy for attacking this problem, but we can indicate some implications of alternative ways of analyzing change which we feel are relevant to the problem. The following discussion will be concerned with two forms of the problem. We shall deal first with the case of comparisons involving two points in time, where initial and terminal measurements on the variables being correlated are obtained for a set of basic areal units, and the longitudinal relationship is determined by correlating the change in one variable with change in the other. Second, we shall examine the situation in which a longitudinal relationship involving a correlation between time series is compared with a cross-sectional relationship holding for a set of areal units at a given time.

Let us begin with the first case in which we have observations on two variables, $X$ and $Y$, for each of $n$ basic areal units; the correlation between change in $X$ and change in $Y$ over a specified time interval, as well as the cross-sectional correlations, is to be determined for the set of $n$ areal units. To make the time element explicit, we shall suppose we have one set of bivariate observations $(X_1, Y_1)$ on the areal units at the initial date of a time period and a corresponding set $(X_2, Y_2)$ at the terminal date. (We are omitting the subscript identifying the areal units and using a single subscript for the time at which the observation is made.) Among the various possible measures of change, the following four are worth mentioning explicitly. The difference between the two observations, $Y_2 - Y_1$, is the conventional *absolute change*. The ratio $Y_2/Y_1$ is a measure of *relative change*, often expressed in the form of a percentage, or proportional, change,

$$\frac{Y_2 - Y_1}{Y_1} = \frac{Y_2}{Y_1} - 1.$$

A measure of *positional change* is obtained by abstracting from the change in dispersion of the variable between the two dates, i.e.,

$$\text{positional change} = y_2 - y_1,$$

where

$$y_2 = \frac{Y_2 - \overline{Y}_2}{\sigma_{Y_2}}$$

and

$$y_1 = \frac{Y_1 - \overline{Y}_1}{\sigma_{Y_1}}.$$

An interesting measure of change which has hitherto received little attention is the *deviational change,*

$$U_y = Y_2 - \hat{Y}_2,$$

where

$$\hat{Y}_2 = a_{Y_2 Y_1} + b_{Y_2 Y_1} Y_1$$

is the value estimated from the inter-annual regression line relating the terminal to the initial value of $Y$.

Of these four measures of change, the relative change is least generally applicable although it is perhaps the measure of change most frequently used. A meaningful measure of relative change can be computed only for a variable measured on a ratio scale, i.e., a scale with truly equal intervals and an absolute zero point. It is obviously inapplicable to the kind of index number in which the location of the zero point is determined arbitrarily. The absolute change measure assumes only an interval scale, a condition often met or assumed for social and economic variables. However, there are cases in which one is willing to assume for sake of convenience that measurement is on an interval scale where it is true, nevertheless, that the variable has a "ceiling." This means that, in principle, it is easier for a change of a given magnitude to occur when the initial observation is small than when it is large. Consequently, a measure of change which takes account of initial level is preferable to the absolute change per se. The measure of positional change accomplishes this insofar as the "ceiling effect" results in an equal contraction of intervals all along the scale. However, the only one of the four change measures that fully takes into account the level at the beginning of the period is the deviational change. Here we assume that deviations are measured from inter-annual regressions taken to be linear in form, but the measure is clearly generalizable to the case of curvilinear inter-annual regressions (see the illustration in Duncan and Cuzzort, 1958).

Where the study design calls for an analysis of the concomitants of change, one obvious procedure is to compute correlations between changes in the dependent variable and changes in one or more independent variables. This point of view brings out some implications of the alternative measures of change. It is important to note that a correlation between changes of two variables can be expressed in terms of certain cross-sectional and inter-annual correlations. It can be shown that the expressions relating a correlation between changes and the set of all possible cross-sectional and inter-annual correlations are as follows, for the four types of change measurement.

(1) Correlations of absolute changes, $(Y_2 - Y_1)$ with $(X_2 - X_1)$:

$$\frac{r_{X_2 Y_2}\sigma_{X_2}\sigma_{Y_2} - r_{X_2 Y_1}\sigma_{X_2}\sigma_{Y_1} - r_{X_1 Y_2}\sigma_{X_1}\sigma_{Y_2} + r_{X_1 Y_1}\sigma_{X_1}\sigma_{Y_1}}{\sqrt{\sigma^2_{X_2} + \sigma^2_{X_1} - 2r_{X_2 X_1}\sigma_{X_2}\sigma_{X_1}} \ \sqrt{\sigma^2_{Y_2} + \sigma^2_{Y_1} - 2r_{Y_2 Y_1}\sigma_{Y_2}\sigma_{Y_1}}}$$

(2) Correlation of relative changes, $Y_2/Y_1$ with $X_2/X_1$:

$$\frac{r_{X_2 Y_2}V_{X_2}V_{Y_2} - r_{X_2 Y_1}V_{X_2}V_{Y_1} - r_{X_1 Y_2}V_{X_1}V_{Y_2} + r_{X_1 Y_1}V_{X_1}V_{Y_1}}{\sqrt{V^2_{X_2} + V^2_{X_1} - 2r_{X_2 X_1}V_{X_2}V_{X_1}} \ \sqrt{V^2_{Y_2} + V^2_{Y_1} - 2r_{Y_2 Y_1}V_{Y_2}V_{Y_1}}}$$

In formula (2), $V$ is the coefficient of variation of the indicated variable, i.e., the standard deviation divided by the mean. The formula is only approximate, in that it neglects certain products of deviations from means, since the means and standard deviations of non-linear functions of two variables can be expressed in terms of the means and standard deviations of the original variables only to a first approximation. The derivation of this formula is based on methods described by Yule (1910).

(3) Correlation of positional changes, $(y_2 - y_1)$ with $(x_2 - x_1)$:

$$\frac{r_{X_2Y_2} - r_{X_2Y_1} - r_{X_1Y_2} + r_{X_1Y_1}}{2\sqrt{1 - r_{X_2X_1}}\ \sqrt{1 - r_{Y_2Y_1}}}$$

(4) Correlation of deviational changes, $U_y$ with $U_x$:

$$\frac{r_{X_2Y_2} - r_{X_2Y_1}r_{Y_2Y_1} - r_{X_1Y_2}r_{X_2X_1} + r_{X_1Y_1}r_{X_2X_1}r_{Y_2Y_1}}{\sqrt{1 - r^2_{X_2X_1}}\ \sqrt{1 - r^2_{Y_2Y_1}}}$$

It can be seen that there is a certain similarity in form of all four expressions. In each case, all six possible intercorrelations of the variables $Y_2$, $Y_1$, $X_2$, and $X_1$ appear in the expression. Expressions (1) and (2) involve the variances of the variables explicitly, whereas this is not true for the expressions (3) and (4). The appearance of the coefficient of variation in expression (2) for the correlation of relative changes emphasizes the inapplicability of this measure of change for variables other than those measured on a ratio scale. There is a marked similarity in the expressions (3) and (4) for correlations of positional and of deviational changes, the difference being that terms in the latter expression have as factors the "stability coefficients" $r_{Y_2Y_1}$ and $r_{X_2X_1}$.

One conclusion to be drawn from the algebra just exhibited is that the interpretation of relationships between changes is not as simple as it might seem intuitively. As a purely descriptive statement, a correlation between changes has a perfectly definite meaning. However, the nature of the interrelationships that determine the magnitude of this correlation is such that various alternative conceptions of the "forces," "influences," or "causes" producing change may be equally plausible, and perhaps equally valid, so far as may be judged solely within the context of the particular observations. Another way of putting this is to state that alternative models of the pattern of change may be consistent with the observations, and the choice among these models must be made on grounds other than the observations themselves. In any case, it is clear that the way in which change is measured is not irrelevant to the way in which it is to be explained.

Thus far we have considered only correlations between changes over a single time period as a means of analyzing longitudinal data. The problem of reconciling longitudinal with cross-sectional relationships, when examined in a more general framework, raises additional issues. Strangely enough, the feature of the problem that seems to be crucial has drawn rather little comment from the writers who have discussed this question. If we think of a longitudinal relationship as one holding between two time series, then the *unit or units for which the longitudinal relationship is hypothesized cannot be the same as those for which the cross-sectional relationship is established.* If we observe, say, families at a given point in time we may find that those making high incomes are saving larger proportions of their incomes than those making low incomes. We are then tempted to infer that if average income rises, the proportion of the average income saved will increase. But in the cross-sectional analysis, the units of observation are individual families or groups of families classified by income; in the longitudinal hypothesis, the unit of observation is the entire aggregate (or population) of families.

The dilemma posed here can be set forth algebraically, making use of the mathematics presented in section 3.1. Let $(X_{it}, Y_{it})$ be a bivariate observation on the $i^{th}$ areal unit in a universe of territory subdivided into n areal units $(i = 1, 2, 3, \ldots n)$ for year, or other period, $t$ $(t = 1, 2, 3, \ldots k)$. Pooling the data for all $k$ years, let $r_t$ be the correlation between $Y$ and $X$ computed over the entire set of $nk$ pairs of values; $r_I$ is then formally equivalent to what W. S. Robinson (1950) calls the "individual correlation." Let $r_{It}$ be the cross-sectional correlation over areal units in a given year, $t$, and let $r_{IT}$ be the "average within-year correlation" (strictly analogous to the "average within-group correlation" in analysis of covariance). Let $r_T$ be the (longitudinal) "between-year" correlation between the yearly averages $\overline{X}_t$ and $\overline{Y}_t$. Analogous definitions of the coefficients of regression of $Y$ on $X$, i.e., $b_I$, $b_{It}$, $b_{IT}$, and $b_T$, can be given. Finally, denote by $E_{YT}$ and $E_{XT}$ the respective correlation ratios of the two variables on years, i.e., the square roots of the ratios of "between-year" to "total" variation. Proceeding directly from these definitions it is easily shown that

$$r_I = r_{IT} \sqrt{1 - E_{YT}^2} \ \sqrt{1 - E_{XT}^2} + r_T E_{YT} E_{XT}$$

and, similarly, that

$$b_I = b_{IT} + E_{XT}^2 \ (b_T - b_{IT}).$$

For simplicity, we are considering all regressions to be linear and are limiting the discussion to the case of only one independent variable.

From the foregoing formulas it is readily seen that, in general, the longitudinal relationship, as represented by the correlation and regression coefficients, $r_T$ and $b_T$, will not be the same as any of the cross-sectional relationships, as summarized by the coefficients $r_I$, $r_{It}$, $r_{IT}$, $b_I$, $b_{It}$, and $b_{IT}$. What is more important, perhaps, is that the longitudinal relationship cannot be inferred from any or all of the cross-sectional relationships by themselves; it is necessary to know the correlation ratios as well. Finally, the formulas indicate that the function connecting the longitudinal with the cross-sectional coefficient involves quantities that can be computed only if cross-sectional data are given for each year rather than merely for a single one of the $k$ years. In some cases, to be sure, the $k$ within-year correlations or regressions (the $r_{It}$'s or the $b_{It}$'s) will not differ significantly from one another and hence any one of them may be used to estimate the average within-year coefficients, $r_{IT}$ and $b_{IT}$. But this need not be the case. It will happen even less frequently that there is no significant difference between the cross-sectional, the between-year, and the within-year coefficients. It is quite possible, for example, for the between-year coefficients to be opposite in sign to the within-year coefficients. It may be noted that the tests of significance ordinarily used in analysis of covariance for ascertaining whether the differences among the $k$ within-year coefficients $b_{It}$ are due to chance would not be strictly applicable here, because the years (corresponding to "treatments" or "groups" in the usual covariance problem) are not independent, inasmuch as the set of areal units is the same from one year to another.

We have indicated that in reasoning from cross-sectional to longitudinal relationships there is not merely a shift from a synchronic to a diachronic viewpoint, but also a shift in the units of observation. However, the only case thus far considered in detail is that in which the cross-sectional relationship is established for areal units making up a universe of territory and the longitudinal relationship concerns aggregate characteristics of that universe (or average characteristics of its component units). There is another important possibility: the longitudinal relationship may concern a single given unit while the cross-sectional relationship involves a whole class of such units. For example, one might have a cross-sectional relationship between infant mortality and accessibility of hospital facilities for the set of

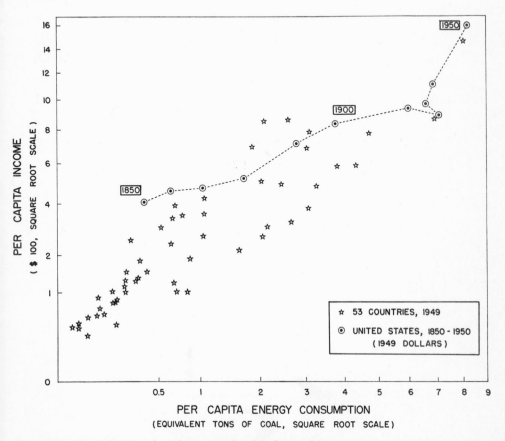

**Figure VI. Cross-Sectional and Longitudinal Relationships of Per Capita Income to Per Capita Consumption of Mineral Fuels and Water Power.** *(Per capita income in hundreds of 1949 United States dollars; per capita energy consumption in coal equivalent in short tons; both variables transformed to square roots; data taken from Dewhurst and Associates, 1955, pp. 40, 51, 1099–1100, 1114.)*

forty-eight States, and convert this to a longitudinal hypothesis concerning the trend in infant mortality in a particular State as it improves its hospital facilities.

Figure VI presents still another example of this kind. Here countries are the units of observation for establishing a cross-sectional relationship between energy consumption and per capita income; the scatterdiagram representing the cross-sectional relationship is shown in comparison with a longitudinal relationship for one of the countries. (There are many serious problems here about the reliability and comparability of the data and about the meaning of international income comparisons; but attention should be focussed on the analytical problem on the assumption that the various measurement problems could be resolved.) In this example the longitudinal relationship appears to be somewhat similar to the cross-sectional; although if linear regression lines were fitted, the two slopes would be somewhat different. But the significant thing to notice is that these data represent only two slices from a theoretical matrix that includes many more observations than are shown. If there are $n$ countries and we are considering $k$ observations in time series for each, the matrix would have $nk$ entries instead of merely the $n$ cross-sectional observations at one date and the $k$ time-series observations for only one country shown here. With the complete matrix a number of questions would arise in addition to that of whether any of the $k$ possible cross-sectional relationships (over countries at a given time) resembles any of the $n$ possible longitudinal relationships (over time for a given country). We would also like to compare the longitudinal relationship for one country with those for the others, to compare the cross-sectional relationship for one year with those for the others, to investigate the $k(k-1)/2$ interannual correlations for either the independent or the dependent variable to ascertain whether the several countries tend to maintain their relative positions over time, and so on. Such questions are, of course, interrelated, although their interrelations are not commonly discussed (see some preliminary notes on the subject in Duncan and Cuzzort, 1958). Perhaps the most closely analogous problem that has been worked out in some detail is that of applying Markov-chain models to such "panel" or mobility data as are obtained in repeated opinion surveys or from data on job changes (T. W. Anderson, 1954; Blumen et al., 1955). The n countries might well be regarded as a "panel."

It may be fitting to conclude this discussion with some remarks on the ways in which investigators have chosen to formulate the relationship between changes in the members of a set of areal units and changes in the entire territorial universe of which they are parts—a problem closely related to the ones we have been discussing.

Vining (1949, pp. 98-99) observes that "the aggregate rate of change is the weighted arithmetic mean of the respective rates of change shown by the component population structures"—i.e., the national rate is a weighted average of the rates for the respective areal units into which the nation is subdivided. On the other hand, Perloff (1957, p. 35) has emphasized that "the whole tempo of development and of economic progress varies from one part of the country to another while all sections are subject to the pervading influence of the national economy and changes within it." The quotation from Vining might suggest a procedure in which change or "growth" was calculated for each areal unit and the national change was then obtained by aggregating these units or by studying the frequency distribution of their changes. Thus, in treating time series of State per capita incomes, Ashby and Spivey (1957) fitted logarithmic trend lines for each of seven regions, obtaining independent estimates of their "growth" components. Carrying a similar procedure one step further, Griliches (1957) fitted logistic trends to annual observations on the percentage of corn acreage planted with hybrid seed in each of a number of States and crop reporting districts. He then correlated estimated parameters of the trend functions with certain explanatory variables observed in the States (or districts) at a given point in time. According to Griliches (1957, p. 503) this procedure followed from the assumption that the time series of acreage planted with hybrid corn consists of observations which

> are not points of equilibrium which may or may not change over time, but points on an adjustment path, moving more or less consistently towards a new equilibrium position. Hence we should phrase our questions in terms of the beginning of the movement, its rate, and its destination. This led to the decision to fit some simple trend functions to the data and concentrate on the explanation of the cross-sectional differences in the estimates of their parameters.

The first of the two studies just mentioned (Ashby and Spivey) makes no reference to possible "national" effects on "regional" changes, while the second (Griliches) takes account of "national" effects only indirectly and does not emphasize them. By contrast, Hanna (1957b), seemingly motivated by considerations like those expressed in the Perloff quotation, sought to measure "growth" in State per capita income by taking the regression of each State's income on that of the nation over a period of years.

The inter-annual regression technique suggested earlier in this section is another approach which tries to get at the "pervading influence of the national economy and changes within it" on the changes in individual areal units. Influences other than those of the "national economy," whether regional or specific to particular areal units or classes thereof, are represented by variation around the inter-annual regression line. Departure of the inter-annual regression from linearity, or departure of the slope of a linear regression from unity, has an interesting interpretation. One would have to say that the pattern of "national growth" was for some areal units to improve (relatively) more rapidly than others or, in some sense, at the expense of others. Thus the use of interannual regression in this context assumes that the areal units are to some degree interrelated parts of a system, so that changes occurring in one are not independent of changes occurring in others. (For further discussion of interannual regressions, see Hanna, 1957a; Duncan and Cuzzort, 1958.)

It is worth remarking that quite high interannual correlations are not inconsistent with the appearance of fairly large variations among areal units in relative rates of change. This is because relative rates have a tendency to "blow up" where the initial observations are low, and also because areal units can differ considerably in rate of change over a period without necessarily altering their rank order positions. Accordingly, in any longitudinal study the investigator has the choice of emphasizing the general stability of a pattern of areal variation, or of focussing on the highly variable rates of change. If either perspective is wholly ignored, the resulting picture is apt to be distorted.

Much of what is oftentimes regarded as "regional effect" in the sense in which that term was used previously (section 3.5) may be conceptualized as a "temporal distribution of rates of growth," i.e., regions ranking high at a given period are those which experienced relatively rapid growth in some preceding period. A temporal perspective on the concept of "region" also is suggested by a viewpoint like that of Hoover and Fisher (1948, p. 4): "The use of any concept of an economic region is justified by the hypothesis that a region grows or decays as an entity, rather than having its changes in income represent merely the random sum of independent experience in individual types of economic activity which happen to be located there." It is probably significant that the contiguity or regional clustering of deviations from interannual regression lines is much less than that of deviations from many cross-sectional regression relationships (Duncan and Cuzzort,1958). It would appear that the attempt to separate considerations of "regional structure" from those of "secular" and "historical" change can yield only partially valid results at best.

# BIBLIOGRAPHY

[*Numbers in brackets following titles refer to text pages where the items are cited.*]

Ackerman, Edward A. 1958. *Geography as a Fundamental Research Discipline,* Research Paper No. 53. Chicago: Department of Geography, University of Chicago. [15].

Anderson, R. L. 1954. "The Problem of Autocorrelation in Regression Analysis," *Journal of the American Statistical Association, 49:* 113–29. [10].

Anderson, T. R. 1955. "Intermetropolitan Migration: A Comparison of the Hypotheses of Zipf and Stouffer," *American Sociological Review, 20:* 287–91. [13, 95].

Anderson, T. W. 1954. "Probability Models for Analyzing Time Changes in Attitudes," in Paul F. Lazarsfeld (ed.). *Mathematical Thinking in the Social Sciences.* Glencoe, Ill.: The Free Press. [171].

Ashby, L. D., and Spivey, W. Allen. 1957. "Gains in Real Per Capita Personal Income: A Method of Analysis," *Southern Economic Journal, 24:* 148–57. [171–72].

Bachi, Roberto. 1957. *Statistical Analysis of Geographical Series.* Jerusalem: Kaplan School, Hebrew University and Central Bureau of Statistics (mimeographed). [90–93].

————. 1958. "Statistical Analysis of Geographical Series," *Bulletin de l'institut international de statistique, 36:* 229–40. [7, 82].

Beach, E. F. 1957. *Economic Models: An Exposition.* New York: John Wiley and Sons. [109].

Bell, Wendell, and Willis, E. M. 1957. "The Segregation of Negroes in American Cities," *Social and Economic Studies, 6:* 59–75. [8].

Bentley, Arthur F. 1926. "Remarks on Method in the Study of Society," *American Journal of Sociology, 32:* 456–60. [3].

Berry, Brian J. L. 1958. "A Note Concerning Methods of Classification," *Annals of the Association of American Geographers, 48:* 300–303. [147].

Birdsell, Joseph B. 1953. "Some Environmental and Cultural Factors Influencing the Structuring of Australian Aboriginal Populations," *American Naturalist, 87* (supplement): 171–207. [27].

Blumen, Isadore, *et al.* 1955. *The Industrial Mobility of Labor as a Probability Process.* Ithaca: Cornell University Press. [171].

Bogue, D. J. 1949. *The Structure of the Metropolitan Community.* Ann Arbor: University of Michigan Press. [52, 95].

————. 1950. "Economic Areas as a Tool for Research and Planning," *American Sociological Review, 15:* 409–16. [12].

————. 1951. *State Economic Areas.* Washington: Government Printing Office. [33, 38, 129, 147, 157].

————. 1954. "An Outline of the Complete System of Economic Areas," *American Journal of Sociology, 60:* 136–39. [12].

————. 1955. "Nodal versus Homogeneous Regions, and Statistical Techniques for Measuring the Influence of Each" (preprint of paper presented at meetings of the International Statistical Institute). [129].

————. 1959a. "Internal Migration," in P. M. Hauser and O. D. Duncan (eds.). *The Study of Population.* Chicago: University of Chicago Press. [34].

————. 1959b. "Population Distribution," in P. M. Hauser and O. D. Duncan (eds.). *The Study of Population.* Chicago: University of Chicago Press. [12, 27–28].

————, and Harris, Dorothy L. 1954. *Comparative Population and Urban Research via Multiple Regression and Covariance Analysis.* Oxford, Ohio: Scripps Foundation. [7, 106, 107].

————, and Thompson, W. S. 1949. "Migration and Distance," *American Sociological Review, 41:* 236–44. [13].

Borts, George H. 1957. "Comment" [on paper with Frank Hanna (1957a)] in *Regional Income* ("Studies of Income and Wealth," Vol. XXI, A Report of the National Bureau of Economic Research). Princeton: Princeton University Press. [122].

Carrothers, Gerald A. P. 1956. "An Historical Review of the Gravity and Potential Concepts of Human Interaction," *Journal of the American Institute of Planners, 22:* 94–102. [14, 97].

Chambliss, Rollin. 1949. "The Geographic Factor in the Human Sex Ratio at Birth," *Social Forces, 28:* 190–95. [113].

Clark, P. J., and Evans, F. C. 1954. "Distance to Nearest Neighbor as a Measure of Spatial Relationships in Populations," *Ecology, 35:* 445–53. [81, 93].

Coombs, Clyde H. 1953. "Theory and Methods of Social Measurement," Chapter 11 in Leon Festinger and Daniel Katz (eds.). *Research Methods in the Behavioral Sciences.* New York: Dryden Press. [42].

Curtis, J. T., and McIntosh, R. P. 1950. "The Interrelations of Certain Analytic and Synthetic Phytosociological Characters," *Ecology, 31:* 434–55. [81].

Dewhurst, J. F., and Associates. 1955. *America's Needs and Resources: A New Survey.* New York: Twentieth Century Fund. [169].

Dice, Lee R. 1952. *Natural Communities.* Ann Arbor: University of Michigan Press. [15].

Duncan, Beverly. 1957. "Population Distribution and Economic Activity: The Nonmetropolitan United States in 1950," unpublished Ph.D. dissertation, University of Chicago (microfilm, University of Chicago Libraries). [154].

Duncan, Otis Dudley. 1948. "Regional Comparisons Standardized for Urbanization," *Social Forces, 26:* 430–33. [63].

————. 1956. "Research on Metropolitan Population: Evaluation of Data," *Journal of the American Statistical Association, 51:* 591–96. [57].

————. 1957a. "The Measurement of Population Distribution," *Population Studies, 11:* 27–45. [22, 55, 80, 81, 82].

————. 1957b. "Population Distribution and Community Structure," *Cold Spring Harbor Symposia on Quantitative Biology, 22:* 357–71. [23, 55, 80, 97].

————. 1959a. "Human Ecology and Population Studies," in P. M. Hauser and O. D. Duncan (eds.). *The Study of Population: An Inventory and Appraisal*. Chicago: University of Chicago Press. [9, 27].

————. 1959b. "Residential Segregation and Social Differentiation," *Proceedings of the International Population Conference, Vienna*. [122, 128].

————, and Cuzzort, Ray P. 1958. "Regional Differentiation and Socio-Economic Change," *Papers and Proceedings of the Regional Science Association, 4:* 163–77. [30, 146, 161, 164, 171, 173, 174].

————, and Davis, Beverly. 1953. "An Alternative to Ecological Correlation," *American Sociological Review, 18:* 665–66. [10, 27].

————, and Duncan, Beverly, 1955a. "Residential Distribution and Occupational Stratification," *American Journal of Sociology, 60:* 493–503 [8, 37].

————, and Duncan, Beverly. 1955b. "A Methodological Analysis of Segregation Indexes," *American Sociological Review, 20:* 210–17. [8, 82].

————, and Duncan, Beverly. 1957. *The Negro Population of Chicago*. Chicago: University of Chicago Press. [10, 129, 161].

————, and Lieberson, Stanley. 1959. "Ethnic Segregation and Assimilation," *American Journal of Sociology, 64:* 364–74. [27].

Ezekiel, Mordecai. 1941. *Methods of Correlation Analysis* (2nd ed.). New York: John Wiley and Sons. [144].

Florence, P. S., *et al.* 1943. "Measures of Industrial Distribution," in National Resources Planning Board, *Industrial Location and National Resources*. Washington: Government Printing Office. [8, 82].

Foley, Donald L. 1953. "Census Tracts and Urban Research," *Journal of the American Statistical Association, 48:* 733–42. [13].

Furfey, P. H. 1927. "Note on Lefever's 'Standard Deviational Ellipse,' " *American Journal of Sociology, 33:* 94–98. [91, 92].

Garrison, William L., and Marble, Duane F. 1958. "Analysis of Highway Networks: A Linear Programming Formulation," *Highway Research Board Proceedings, 37:* 1–17. [95].

Geary, R. C. 1954. "The Contiguity Ratio and Statistical Mapping," *The Incorporated Statistician, 5:* 115–45. [11, 131–34, 137].

Godlund, Sven. 1956. *The Function and Growth of Bus Traffic within the Sphere of Urban Influence* ("Lund Studies in Geography," Ser. B., "Human Geography," No. 18). Lund: C. W. K. Gleerup. [95].

Goodall, D. W. 1952. "Quantitative Aspects of Plant Distribution," *Biological Reviews of the Cambridge Philosophical Society, 27:* 194–245. [7, 9, 81].

Goodman, Leo A. 1953. "Ecological Regression and Behavior of Individuals," *American Sociological Review, 18:* 663–64. [10, 27, 68].

————. 1959. "Some Alternatives to Ecological Correlation," *American Journal of Sociology, 64:* 610–25, [27, 68].

Gosnell, H. F., and Schmidt, M. J. 1936. "Factorial and Correlational Analysis of the 1934 Vote in Chicago," *Journal of the American Statistical Association, 31:* 507–18. [13].

Greig-Smith, P. 1957. *Quantitative Plant Ecology.* New York: Academic Press. [7].

Griliches, Zvi. 1957. "Hybrid Corn: An Exploration in the Economics of Technological Change," *Econometrica, 25:* 501–22. [11, 172].

Hägerstrand, Torsten. 1952. *The Propagation of Innovation Waves* ("Lund Studies in Geography," Ser. B., "Human Geography," No. 4). Lund: Department of Geography, Royal University of Lund. [95].

Hagood, Margaret J. 1943. "Statistical Methods for Delineation of Regions Applied to Data on Agriculture and Population," *Social Forces, 21:* 287–97. [12, 129, 147].

————, and Bernert, Eleanor H. 1945. "Component Indexes as a Basis for Stratification in Sampling," *Journal of the American Statistical Association, 40:* 330–41. [157].

————, *et al.* 1941. "An Examination of the Use of Factor Analysis in the Problem of Subregional Delineation," *Rural Sociology, 6:* 216–33. [129].

Hagood, Margaret J., *et al.* 1957. *Farm-Operator Family Level-of-Living Indexes for Counties of the United States, 1945, 1950, and 1954* ("Statistical Bulletin," No. 204.) Washington: Agricultural Marketing Service. [50].

Halbwachs, Maurice. 1960. *Population and Society: Introduction to Social Morphology* (trans. Otis Dudley Duncan and Harold W. Pfautz). Glencoe, Ill.: Free Press. [16].

Hanna, Frank A. 1957a. "Analysis of Interstate Income Differentials: Theory and Practice," in *Regional Income* ("Studies in Income and Wealth," Vol. XXI. A Report of the National Bureau of Economic Research). Princeton: Princeton University Press. [122, 173].

————. 1957b. "Relative Growth among Regions" (preprint of paper presented at meetings of the International Statistical Institute). [12, 96, 172].

Hannerberg, D., Hägerstrand, T., and Odeving, B. (eds.). 1957. *Migration in Sweden: A Symposium* ("Lund Studies in Geography," Ser. B., "Human Geography," No. 13.) Lund: C. W. K. Gleerup. [14, 95].

Harris, C. D. 1954. "The Market as a Factor in the Localization of Industry in the United States," *Annals of the Association of American Geographers, 44:* 315–48. [55, 97].

Hart, J. F. 1954. "Central Tendency in Areal Distributions," *Economic Geography, 30:* 48–59. [82].

Hartshorne, Richard. 1949. *The Nature of Geography* (2nd ed.). Lancaster, Pa.: Association of American Geographers. [12, 19, 20, 37].

Hatt, P. K. 1946. "The Concept of Natural Area," *American Sociological Review, 11:* 423–28. [98].

Hauser, P. M., Duncan, O. D., and Duncan, B. D. 1956. *Methods of Urban Analysis.* San Antonio: Air Force Personnel and Training Research Center. [7, 82, 93].

Hawley, A. H. 1950. *Human Ecology: A Theory of Community Structure.* New York: Ronald Press. [21, 22].

————, and Duncan, O. D. 1957. "Social Area Analysis: A Critical Appraisal," *Land Economics, 33:* 337–45. [38, 98].

Hogben, Lancelot (ed.). 1938. *Political Arithmetic*. London: George Allen and Unwin. [32].

Holt, Charles C. 1954. Book review of G. Tintner's *Mathematics and Statistics for Economists, American Economic Review, 44:* 433–35. [104].

Hoover, E. M. 1936. "The Measurement of Industrial Localization," *Review of Economic Statistics, 18:* 162–71. [8].

————. 1941. "Interstate Redistribution of Population, 1850–1940," *Journal of Economic History, 1:* 199–205. [83].

————. 1951. "Internal Mobility and the Location of Industry," in H. F. Williamson (ed.). *The Growth of the American Economy* (2nd ed.). New York: Prentice-Hall. [83].

————. 1957. "Comment" [on H. S. Perloff's *Regional Income* (1957)] in "Studies in Income and Wealth," Vol. XXI). Princeton: Princeton University Press. [64].

————, and Fisher, J. L. 1948. "Regional Aspects of Economic Growth and Decay," New York: National Bureau of Economic Research (mimeographed). [173–74].

Hutchinson, E. P. 1956. *Immigrants and Their Children, 1850–1950*. New York: John Wiley and Sons. [9].

Isard, Walter. 1951. "Interregional and Regional Input-Output Analysis: A Model of a Space-Economy," *Review of Economics and Statistics, 33:* 318–28. [56, 96].

————. 1956. "Regional Science, the Concept of Region, and Regional Structure," *Papers and Proceedings of the Regional Science Association, 2:* 13–26. [11, 98, 147].

————, and Whitney, Vincent. 1949. "Metropolitan Site Selection," *Social Forces, 27:* 263–69. [95].

Isbell, Eleanor C. 1944. "Internal Migration in Sweden and Intervening Opportunities," *American Sociological Review, 9:* 627–39. [13, 95].

Jahn, Julius A., *et al.* 1947. "The Measurement of Ecological Segregation," *American Sociological Review, 12:* 293–303. [8].

James, P. E. 1954. "The Geographic Study of Population," in P. E. James and C. F. Jones (eds.). *American Geography: Inventory and Prospect*. Syracuse: Syracuse University Press. [81].

James, P. E. 1958. "Discussion: The Core and Boundaries of Regional Science," *Papers and Proceedings of the Regional Science Association, 4:* 23–26. [4, 39].

———, and Jones, C. F. (eds.). 1954. *American Geography: Inventory and Prospect*. Syracuse: Syracuse University Press. [12, 25, 98, 147, 159].

Kendall, M. G. 1939. "The Geographical Distribution of Crop Productivity in England," *Journal of the Royal Statistical Society, 102:* 21–62. [117, 129].

———. 1947. *The Advanced Theory of Statistics* (3rd ed.). London: Griffin & Co. [132].

Kendall, Patricia L., and Lazarsfeld, P. F. 1955. "The Relation between Individual and Group Characteristics in *The American Soldier*," in P. F. Lazarsfeld and Morris Rosenberg (eds.). *The Language of Social Research*. Glencoe, Ill.: The Free Press. [9, 41].

Kish, Leslie. 1954. "Differentiation in Metropolitan Areas," *American Sociological Review, 19:* 388–98. [38].

Kitagawa, Evelyn M. 1955. "Components of a Difference between Two Rates," *Journal of the American Statistical Association, 50:* 1168–94. [63, 115].

Kontkanen, Paavo. 1957. "On the Delimitation of Communities in Research on Animal Biocoenotics," *Cold Spring Harbor Symposia on Quantitative Biology, 22:* 373–78. [9].

Kulldorff, Gunnar. 1955. *Migration Probabilities* ("Lund Studies in Geography," Ser. B, "Human Geography," No. 14.) Lund: C. W. K. Gleerup. [34].

Lee, E. S., *et al.* 1957. *Population Redistribution and Economic Growth*, Vol. I. Philadelphia: American Philosophical Society. [58, 135].

McCarty, H. H., Hook, J. C., and Knos, D. S. 1956. *The Measurement of Association in Industrial Geography*. Iowa City: Department of Geography, State University of Iowa. [10, 49, 106, 111].

Maitland, Sheridan T., and Fisher, Dorothy Anne. 1958. *Area Variations in the Wages of Agricultural Labor in the United States* ("United States Department of Agriculture Technical Bulletin," No. 1177.) Washington: Government Printing Office. [145].

Menzel, Herbert. 1950. "Comment on Robinson's 'Ecological Correlations and the Behavior of Individuals,' " *American Sociological Review, 15:* 674. [27].

Myers, J. K. 1954. "Note on the Homogeneity of Census Tracts: A Methodological Problem in Urban Ecological Research," *Social Forces, 32:* 364–66. [38].

Park, Robert E. 1952. *Human Communities: The City and Human Ecology.* Glencoe, Ill.: The Free Press. [16].

Perloff, Harvey S. 1957. "Problems of Assessing Regional Economic Progress," *Regional Income* ("Studies in Income and Wealth," Vol. XXI.) Princeton: Princeton University Press. [11–12, 147, 171].

———. 1958. "Interrelations of State Income and Industrial Structure," *Review of Economics and Statistics, 39:* 162–71. [122].

Price, Daniel O. 1948. "Distance and Direction as Vectors of Internal Migration, 1935–1940," *Social Forces, 27:* 48–53. [13].

Proctor, C. H., and Loomis, C. P. 1951. "Analysis of Sociometric Data," in Marie Jahoda, *et al., Research Methods in Social Relations,* Part II. New York: Dryden Press. [45].

Quinn, J. A. 1950. *Human Ecology.* New York: Prentice-Hall. [13].

Rapoport, Anatol. 1957. "Lewis F. Richardson's Mathematical Theory of War," *Journal of Conflict Resolution, 1:* 249–99. [99].

Ravenstein, E. G. 1885–89. "The Laws of Migration," *Journal of the Royal Statistical Society, 48:* 167–235; *52:* 241–305. [13].

Reynolds, Robert B. 1956. "Statistical Methods in Geographical Research," *Geographical Review, 46:* 129–31. [7].

Robinson, A. H. 1956. "The Necessity of Weighting Values in Correlation Analysis of Areal Data," *Annals of the As-*

*sociation of American Geographers, 46:* 233–36. [47, 51, 124].

————, and Bryson, R. A. 1957. "A Method for Describing Quantitatively the Correspondence of Geographical Distributions," *Annals of the Association of American Geographers, 47:* 379–91. [106].

Robinson, W. S. 1950. "Ecological Correlations and the Behavior of Individuals," *American Sociological Review, 15:* 351–57. [9, 10, 26, 27, 65, 67, 167].

Ruttan, V. W. 1955. "The Impact of Urban-Industrial Development on Agriculture in the Tennessee Valley and the Southeast," *Papers and Proceedings of the Regional Science Association, 1:* R1–R23. [106].

Sanderson, Fred H. 1954. *Methods of Crop Forecasting.* Cambridge: Harvard University Press. [11, 18–19, 106, 107].

Schmid, C. F., and MacCannell, E. H. 1955. "Basic Problems, Techniques, and Theory of Isopleth Mapping," *Journal of the American Statistical Association, 50:* 220–39. [149].

Shevsky, Eshref, and Bell, Wendell. 1955. *Social Area Analysis.* Stanford: Stanford University Press. [7, 158].

Simiand, François. 1932. *Le salaire, l'évolution sociale, et la monnaie,* Vol. I. Paris: Alcan. [160].

Simon, H. A. 1957. *Models of Man.* New York: John Wiley and Sons. [108, 146].

Smith, Harry, Jr. 1954. "Weighting Coefficients for Age-Adjusted Death Rates," unpublished Ph.D. dissertation, Department of Statistics, North Carolina State College, Raleigh, N.C. (microfilm available from Photoreproduction Service, University of North Carolina Library, Chapel Hill, N. C.). [117].

Smith, Joel. 1954. "A Method for the Classification of Areas on the Basis of Demographically Homogeneous Populations," *American Sociological Review, 19:* 201–207. [38].

Stephan, F. F. 1934. "Sampling Errors and the Interpretation of Social Data Ordered in Time and Space," *Journal of the American Statistical Association, 29:* 165–66. [10, 129].

Stewart, John Q. 1947. "Empirical Mathematical Rules Concerning the Distribution and Equilibrium of Population," *Geographical Review, 37:* 461–85. [55].

———. 1948. "Demographic Gravitation: Evidence and Applications," *Sociometry, 11:* 31–58. [14].

———, and Warntz, William. 1958. "Physics of *Population* Distribution," *Journal of Regional Science, 1:* 99–123. [7, 97].

Stouffer, S. A. 1940. "Intervening Opportunities: A Theory Relating Mobility and Distance," *American Sociological Review, 5:* 845–67. [13, 94].

Strand, E. G., and Heady, E. O. 1955. *Productivity of Resources Used on Commercial Farms* ("United States Department of Agriculture, Technical Bulletin" No. 1128). Washington: Government Printing Office. [158].

Suits, D. B. 1957. "Use of Dummy Variables in Regression Equations," *Journal of the American Statistical Association, 52:* 548–51. [142–43].

Sviatlovsky, E. E., and Eells, W. C. 1937. "The Centrographical Method and Regional Analysis," *Geographical Review, 27:* 240–54. [82].

Theil, H. 1954. *Linear Aggregation of Economic Relations.* Amsterdam: North-Holland Publishing Co. [9, 10, 67].

Thomas, Morgan D. 1958. "Discussion: Methodological Issues in Regional Science," *Papers and Proceedings of the Regional Science Association, 4:* 199–202. [147].

Thompson, W. R. 1953. "The Measurement of Industry Location Patterns," unpublished Ph.D. dissertation, University of Michigan. [8, 82].

Tryon, Robert C. 1955. *Identification of Social Areas by Cluster Analysis.* Berkeley: University of California Publications in Psychology. Vol. VIII. (No. 1). [13, 38].

Ullman, E. L. 1957. *American Commodity Flow.* Seattle: University of Washington Press. [56].

United States Bureau of the Census. 1958. *Census Tract Manual* (4th ed.). Washington: Government Printing Office. [13].

United States National Office of Vital Statistics. 1954. "Weight at Birth and its Effect on Survival of the Newborn in the United States, Early 1950," *Vital Statistics—Special Reports, 39:* 1–33. [73].

Varley, David W. 1956. "A Quantitative Analysis of Regionalism in the United States, 1940," unpublished Ph.D. dissertation, University of Michigan. [38, 145].

Vining, Rutledge. 1949. "The Region as an Economic Entity and Certain Variations to be Observed in the Study of Systems of Regions," *American Economic Review, 39:* 89–104. [11, 95, 171].

―――. 1953. "Delimitation of Economic Areas: Statistical Conceptions in the Study of the Spatial Structure of an Economic System," *Journal of the American Statistical Association, 48:* 44–64. [23, 95–96, 98, 103–4].

―――. 1955. "A Description of Certain Spatial Aspects of an Economic System," *Economic Development and Cultural Change, 3:* 147–95. [23, 24, 95].

Walker, Helen M., and Lev, Joseph. 1953. *Statistical Inference.* New York: Henry Holt and Co. [142–44].

Weatherford, Willis D., Jr. 1957. *Geographic Differentials of Agricultural Wages in the United States.* Cambridge: Harvard University Press. [17].

Whittle, P. 1954. "On Stationary Processes in the Plane," *Biometrika, 41:* 434 (abstract by W. L. Smith, *Journal of the American Statistical Association, 50:* 606). [11].

Wold, Herman, 1956. "Causal Inference from Observational Data," *Journal of the Royal Statistical Society,* Series A, *119:* 28–61. [108].

Wooldridge, S. W., and East, W. Gordon. 1951. *The Spirit and Purpose of Geography.* London: Hutchinson's University Library. [14–15].

Wright, J. K. 1937. "Some Measures of Distributions," *Annals of the Association of American Geographers, 27:* 177–211. [8, 82, 93].

Yule, G. U. 1910. "On the Interpretation of Correlations between Indices or Ratios," *Journal of the Royal Statistical Society, 73:* 644–47. [164].

————, and Kendall, M. G. 1950. *An Introduction to the Theory of Statistics* (14th ed.). New York: Hafner Publishing Co. [91, 109–10, 117].

Zipf, G. K. 1946. "The $P_1P_2/D$ Hypothesis: On the Intercity Movement of Persons," *American Sociological Review, 11:* 677–86. [14].

# SUBJECT INDEX

[For Author Index, *see* Bibliography]

Division of labor, 17, 95
Dummy variable, 142–43

Ecological correlation, 9–10, 26–
    27, 65–67
Econometrics, 109, 147
Ecosystem, 15
Energy consumption, 169–70
Ethnic composition, 122ff.
Exogenous variable, 75–77
Expected cases, 120ff.
Explanation, 17, 21, 23–24, 27–
    28, 61, 92, 97–98, 99ff.,
    134, 146, 150

Flow, 13–14, 22, 25, 56, 95–96

Geography, 6, 14–15, 19–21
Gravity model, 14, 97
Growth, 171–72

Homogeneity, 12, 37–38, 129,
    147
Hospitalization of births, 69, 72,
    74–75, 119, 168
Human ecology, 12–13, 16, 23,
    27
Hypothesis formation, 106

Incidence matrix, 115
Income, 17, 23, 43, 44, 51–52,
    76–77, 130, 141ff., 166,
    169–70
Index number, 46, 117–18
Index of concentration, 83ff.
Indirect standardization, 118

Industry, 59
Infant mortality, 69ff., 108, 113,
    119, 134ff., 141ff., 168
Input-output model, 96, 98
Interaction, 63–64
Intervening opportunities, 13, 94
Isoline, 53–54, 149
Isopleth, 37, 148–49

Land use, 48, 130, 154–57
Level of living, 30, 50, 111, 161
Location, 21–22, 39–40, 48–49,
    52ff.
Localization, coefficient of, 8, 82
Longitudinal analysis, 30, 160ff.

Map, 15, 29, 53–54, 81, 92, 136
Matrix, 114ff., 170
Mechanization, 30, 161
Methodology, 3, 28–29
Migration, 34, 42, 44, 56, 88,
    90, 94–95
Model, 17, 61, 69ff., 94, 101,
    105
Modifiable unit, 78, 109
Mortality, 100–2, 111, 118

Nearest neighbor, 81, 129–30
Neonatal mortality, 73

Phytosociology, 81
Policy, 103–4
Population, 8, 16, 21–22, 28,
    39, 41ff., 113ff.
Potential of population, 53–55,
    82, 97, 148, 156